WARRIOR

FIRST EDITION

Copyright © Geoff Thompson 2010

Geoff Thompson has asserted his right under the
Copyright, Designs and Patents Act 1988 to be identified
as the author of this work.

Proudly published in Great Britain by
Snowbooks Ltd.
9B Kirtlington Business Centre
Oxford OX5 3JA
www.snowbooks.com

A CIP catalogue record for this book
is available from the British Library

ISBN 978-1-90672-918

www.geoffthompson.com

Printed and bound in the UK by J F Print Ltd., Sparkford

WARRIOR

A Path to Self-Sovereignty

GEOFF THOMPSON

Dedication

To Sharon - my alpha and my omega

Author Biography

Until the age of 30, Geoff Thompson had worked through a plethora of menial jobs, from glass collector to floor sweeper—even spending a decade working as a nightclub bouncer.

Convinced there must be more to life than this, Geoff decided to become a martial arts instructor. He is now a 7th-dan, black belt, and, according to *Black Belt* magazine USA, is the most influential martial artist in the world after Bruce Lee.

He followed this accomplishment by living out his dream to become a professional writer. Not only is he the author of 34 books, he also wrote five multi-award-winning films (one BAFTA nominated, one BAFTA winning), three stage plays and hundreds of articles that have been published in a variety of publications. Additionally, he penned a monthly column in *Men's Fitness Magazine* for two years, as well as features and profiles in many broadsheet newspapers, including *The Times*.

Geoff's autobiography, *Watch My Back*, has been adapted into a major motion picture, *Clubbed*.

His latest multi award-winning film, *Romans 12:20*, qualified for the Oscar Long List 2010 for best film in the short category.

Geoff lives with his wife, (business partner and best mate) Sharon, between Coventry (middle England) and Islington, London.

I Live My Life in Growing Orbits

Rainer Maria Rilke

"I live my life in growing orbits
Which move out over the things of the world
Perhaps I can never achieve the last
But that will be my attempt
I am circling around God
Around the ancient tower
And I have been circling for a thousand years
And I still don't know if I am a falcon, or a storm, or a
great song.

Contents

PREFACE

The world is changing. Have you noticed? We are no longer at the bottom of the food chain. The tigers, the lions, and the man-enemies of antiquity are safely caged and emasculated in public zoos and national parks. But new enemies have emerged. They are insidious; their teeth twice as sharp and masters of stealth.

I am talking, of course, about the illnesses, viruses, and diseases that largely exist in contemporary society due to man's penchant for excessive consumption and his lack of physical activity. With the need for hunting, gathering and living off our wits rapidly declining, the under-used physical body is becoming less of a sinewy working tool and more of a cumbersome liability. We have lost, not only our desire for the warrior mentality, we have lost our reason for it. Certainly we have lost our tolerance for discomfort, and without that, we are all dead men walking.

The body, once an inhospitable environ for malady, is now a breeding ground for disease. Infirmity is kicking sand in all our faces. This has to change if we are to survive as a species.

INTRODUCTION

Where have all the warriors gone?

Where are all the stoics, the hardy grafters, the industrious inventors, the pioneers, and adventurers? Why are men's shirts stretched at the belly instead of tight on the chest and back? And why are woman having to place post codes on each cheek of their very large bottoms? Whatever happened to physical prowess, the hardy mentality, and the imaginative acuity that enabled our great species to survive eons against seemingly impossible odds?

Watching the old film, *The Last of the Mohicans*, starring Daniel Day Lewis, I was amazed how these stoics dealt with their harrowing circumstance in history. It was an incredibly inspiring film, a moving and visceral account of the dying Mohican race, that instilled in me a need to reconnect with my warrior ancestry. As I watched the film, I kept reflecting on life in the twenty-first century and thinking, *'where have all the warriors gone?'* These sinewy men and svelte women lived a challenging and purposeful existence, and they were all the more vibrant and passionate for it.

People today, by comparison, have become slobbish and

lazy, moaners, and whingers of the first order. They have forgotten how to break a sweat, and they don't know how to handle discomfort anymore. At the first sign of distress, they run to the pub or the doctor, or smother their hurt under blankets of addiction.

Daniel Day Lewis would be ashamed!

Ours may be a sedentary society, but we still live in a body that is built to move. The body needs physically demanding work in order to stay healthy. Equally, the mind needs challenge and purpose. The hunter-gatherer that once roamed the plains and jungles with arrow and spear is still inside us. It is a vital and untapped resource, part of our heritage that needs recognition and expression. Re-claiming this legacy is vital for the physical, mental, and spiritual well-being of our species. The pulsing vitality derived from expressing our inner warrior spawns a confidence and a congruence that will permeate through every aspect of our lives—whether in the work place, at home, or in a dark alley facing down and angry mugger.

People have forgotten how to be courageous. They have forgotten why it is important to be courageous.

Warrior is a simple step-by-step guide to re-booting purpose and reclaiming our warriorship.

This is a book for any man. This is a read for every man. It is also a book for women—they need to be warriors too. If you are living in the world, then you need to be able to survive in the world. Who can do that safely and profitably if they are not warriors?

Anyone conflicted and lost in the maze that is the human condition will be able to grow from these pages—*if* they use the information. It is not enough to *know*. You need to *act*.

It is interesting to note the rapid decline of the 'lowest common denominator' lad's mag. At the time of the writing of this book, sales of those that specialise in titillation over content are declining, while the more informed and responsible men's fitness type magazines are increasing. *Men's Health Magazine*, for instance, now sells more copies per calendar month than any of the tabloid glossies. Even the leviathans that have dominated the male magazine market for the last decade are now chasing, rather than leading. It seems men are now looking towards their health and well-being more than they are the latest bikini-clad soap star on the cover of a porn-mag hidden inside the Trojan horse of an entertainment monthly.

It has also been widely reported that woman, when looking for 'a good pro-creational mate,' are choosing muscle over money, swapping their very rich city boyfriends for men of a more practical and physical nature. Plumbers, builders, and handy-men are the new vogue, though I suspect the girls would prefer a hybrid of the two: someone that can throw a spear *and* fill out a spread sheet.

Women are also starting to realise their own worth in the world and in the work place, frequently outclassing their male counterparts in the board room. Ladies are even catching us in the arena of sport. There are very few men in the world of marathon running for instance—even on the world stage—that can outpace Paula Radcliffe.

The world is still a jungle full of man eaters, of that I am sure. Even if the terrain and the enemy *have* changed shape, so the need for warriorship has never been more imperative. The desire is there. People only lack a reliable road map.

Chapter One

†

A Warrior...
Seeks a Difficult Life

The Buddha said that life is hard. Of course we all know this is true. Even though we search far and wide for the easy life, we always seem to end up on a rock, a hard place, or somewhere betwixt the two.

I spent my youth trying to combat fear. I went into frightening places to face down my nemesis, and I warred in many a battle theatre. But I did not lose my fear. I searched far and wide for a life without pain and discomfort, using mostly avoidance techniques. I became expert at running away, rolling over, and taking slaps on both cheeks. None of it diminished the pain and discomfort of being in the world one bit. In fact the discomfort increased disproportionately. My experiences taught me a life-changing lesson, one that is so anti-intuitive most people miss it. Fear, pain, and discomfort are not supposed to be cured like a virus or shed like an old skin—they are there to be embraced.

When faced and mastered they can act like fertiliser for self development. Comfort is the terrorist in our lives. There is no growth in it. All the growth, all the gold, all the bounty is concealed in a place most people fear to look. Discomfort.

Embracing discomfort develops hardiness and forges a character that cannot be cast in any other way. If you strip away the incendiary labels from these supposedly anomalous emotions and feelings you are left with a very valuable commodity: energy.

Fear is energy. Discomfort is energy. Anxiety is energy. Everything is energy, disguising itself in different shapes and concealing its true identity under many pseudonyms. When I finally understood this, when I realised the power of discomfort, I stopped trying to strip it from my life. I stopped trying to avoid the pain and the fear, and instead I became an alchemist. I used this base energy, and transmuted it into success.

This chapter is about identifying the difficult areas of your life and embracing them. In fact, I recommend that you make a list. Write down on a piece of paper and physically 'out' all the difficult life situations you are avoiding. Once they are written down and identified you will be surprised at how much power you'll be able to exert over them. Identifying your weak areas, admitting them, is the very first step to empowerment. The solutions to our problems are usually hidden in the problems themselves.

It is also about changing our perception of discomfort and learning to accept, like, and—if we want to become very successful—love, discomfort.

Take a top-end body builder, for instance. They understand that muscle growth is in the burn, so the last few repetitions of a training set is all they seek. They have learned to associate pain with gain. Most people go into the gym and spend two hours moving from one exercise to another, often socialising between sets. They work on the outer edges of the burn, but never actually stay there for very long. During a 120- minute session they probably only get about half an hour's worth of sweat. From my observation, out of that 30 minutes, they hardly ever get a good, hardy burn. They go into the gym looking for a physique, and spend the majority of their workout avoiding the one and only thing that will give it to them—the burn. This is because the burn hurts. It is uncomfortable. Their life is, or has been, about avoiding discomfort because they have the wrong perception of it. I have lost count of the number of people I know who have invested years in gym training and membership, but still have no quality physique.

The next uncomfortable aspect of building a physique they avoid is a healthy diet. Eating the right food is probably 80 percent of the battle as far as shape and health are concerned. People are educated about diet by the experts in their gym, but they still do not incorporate the correct eating habits into their life because, of course, it is very uncomfortable to eat healthily.

People with great potential do not grow a nice physique because they avoid discomfort. They avoid discomfort because they have the wrong perception of discomfort. The practised builder of physiques understands where the growth is. His perception of the burn is not that it is pain, but rather, that it is growth. He goes into the gym, finds the burn very quickly, and stays in the burn long. Afterwards, he talks about how great the burn was and what a tortuously difficult session it was. He or she even designs specific training methods that will get them into the burn quicker and keep them there longer. They get excited about developing killer exercises that isolate specific muscles, and keep them in a state of suspended burn. The practiced folk spend less time in the gym than most people, but they get 10 times as much done.

After training they *get off* on their ability to be disciplined with food by mastering their palate. Placing only the very best food into their bodies, they turn the discomfort most people associate with any kind of diet into absolute and unequivocal pleasure. They know that if the diet is not right, then all that hard training will have been wasted. These masters make it their vocation to be the best trained and the most informed people on this spinning planet as far as the body is concerned.

These folks live their life in a place of discomfort, but they are so comfortable with it that it is no longer uncomfortable. The severe discipline does not feel severe to them. It is just a way of life, one they love and thrive on. They do not feel as though they have given up any luxury—quite the opposite in fact. They know they have escaped from it. The luxury, the comfort, the easy life is actually a trap, a prison for the weak-of-will and the easily convinced. Comfort is the addiction of the twenty-first century and it's killing us a species. Actually, it is not just the comfort, it is the denial. Whether the addiction is to alcohol, drugs, junk food, or sex, most addicts I know are in denial of their disease. *That* is what's killing them. If you don't admit that you have a problem, then what chance have you of solving it? To overcome an addiction, you first have to admit that you have a problem in the first place.

Wake up!

Stop wasting your life waiting for the fat to fall off all by its self, or for the physique to grow of its own accord. Stop waiting for your job prospects to improve without your help, or for your marriage to be happy, without any positive input from you. Seek a difficult life. That is where the growth is. People keep doing the same old thing day in and day out, expecting different results. If you keep planting dandelion seeds you will keep growing dandelions. Do not expect roses.

One of the laws of Hermes states: 'As within as without.' What you are on the inside is what you will see projected all around you. The warrior learns this lesson fast and acts upon it. If you don't like what you see out there, change yourself from the inside.

Any kind of change is going to involve discomfort. That is fact. Change is one of the greatest fears we experience as a species, but here is the thing. Change is going to happen anyway. Change is a given, the one thing you can be sure of—guaranteed. Since it is certain and inevitable, we may as well embrace it and become a part of the positive change that we would like to see in our lives.

Ghandi suggested that we become the change we want to see.

The principle of growth through discomfort carries across to all things. Whether you are working on your physique or your marriage, your business or your health, the growth that comes from discomfort is what most of us avoid on a daily basis.

Becoming a great business man is no different from developing a great physique. The growth is in the burn. Again, most people play at business, and spend most of their time avoiding the uncomfortable things that are going to grow their empire most. Instead, they concentrate on being very busy working on the wrong things. Folks who fail in business are often very hard-working people, but hard working in all the wrong directions. They get brilliantly and prolifically busy doing the things that will not help them grow, whilst blatantly avoiding the difficult aspects that will.

A friend of mine who wants to build his business, came to me for advice, knowing I would be honest and give him some truth. Though hard working and dedicated, he has asked me for the same advice almost a dozen times now, and has still not incorporated any of my suggestions into his business. As I see it, there is one glaring problem that he needs to address. Understanding his business as I do, I know that this one aspect alone, over time, will transform his client base.

Obviously, the change is uncomfortable for him. It requires new learning in an area he is unfamiliar with, and it means investing a small amount of capital he says he doesn't have. I made the point that his discomfort is a good sign— not a bad sign—because it is where the expansion is. The very fact that my suggestion is uncomfortable for him should tell him something. I reminded him that his life is difficult at the moment anyway. By incorporating my suggestion and leaning into the difficulty, he would be driving it, taking control of it, and using the energy of discomfort to fire his progression.

He didn't take my suggestion. I'd like to tell you that it worked out anyway, or that he is, at the very least, still where he was when we last spoke. But he isn't. He has actually slipped backwards. One of the inevitable truths about change is that it is like time and the tides—it waits for no man.

I have another friend in a similar business, who also rings

me periodically for advice. Even though every piece of advice I offer is uncomfortable for him, he incorporates it anyway. His business is growing at a heady rate. He is a martial artist and understands pain. He has a healthy relationship with it and knows that where there is discomfort, there is gold. He is successful, not despite his discomfort, but because of it.

He is a man that seeks a difficult life. In fact he thrives on difficulty. That is why he takes the advice and uses a *discomfort barometer* as an indicator. If it makes him feel very uncomfortable, he smiles because he knows that he is onto something. Which brings up an interesting point: When you offer advice to people and they take it and use it, you feel a great desire to help them again the next time they ask. The more they invest your advice into their lives, the more you want to help. For those that do nothing with your offerings, you feel less and less inclined to proffer more.

In the Biblical parable of the talents, Jesus of Nazareth said that *those who have are given more, and those who have not, it is taken away from them.* When you use and invest your information (your talents), more will be given to you. But if you sit on or bury your talents, they will eventually atrophy.

In simpler terms—use it or lose it.

» Anabolic and catabolic discomfort.

Not all discomfort is good for you. There is an old saying and it holds true: Anything that does not kill you will make you stronger. I like this saying, but there is a hidden caveat that involves discomfort. Some kinds of discomfort break you down and keep breaking you down, whilst other kinds of discomfort break you down in order to build you up again.

I worked in a factory sweeping floors for two years. The job paid a wage for which I was grateful, but I did not like the job. It was unfulfilling. I felt under employed, like a Formula 1 race car that was being used just for a Sunday jaunt. I was working way below my potential. The point is, the job was boring, but comfortable. I hated it, but I made the bills. It was unfulfilling, but it was reliable. It was an uncomfortable job, but the discomfort was not growing me. I was not growing at all.

I would consider this to be a catabolic discomfort. My wisdom told me that there was no growing potential there, that I should find a bigger pot in which to plant myself. By staying at this job, I knew I would risk the stifling root-bound inevitability that sweeping floors in a factory promised. Most people I meet are in this position, doing jobs that pay the bills but do not satisfy the soul. The job does not excite them, and certainly they do not grow.

Another kind of catabolic discomfort is when people lift too much weight too soon, or lift a weight that stretches and breaks down the muscle so they do not recuperate afterwards. One of the fundamental laws of growth is rest. Bodybuilders know that rest and sleep are vital ingredients in building quality muscles. It is no good putting yourself in the burn day in and day out if you are not going to allow the muscle to rest and re-build.

Maximum growth demands a good balance of hard work, hard rest, and hard play. Many people injure themselves in training and make themselves ill in business when they do not observe this law. The balance is delicate and not one that is easy to articulate in a book or words. It is something that comes with wisdom. Wisdom is earned, the processed product of extensive periods in the theatre of life.

Wisdom is about learning to listen to your body, because your body is talking to you all the time. If you are getting injuries and ailments and illnesses, your body is telling you something. Either you are going too fast or too slow, too hard or too soft, or you are pushing when you should be yielding. Your body is a beautiful organism. It is ultimately wise—if you listen to it—and will give you lots of subtle warnings if you fall out of balance. A gentle plod here, a shot across the bow there—or, if you don't listen—an out-and-out, stop-you-in-your-tracks illness or injury. Similarly it is about heeding your natural instinct, that small quiet voice that often gets drowned out by the incessant noise of fear, haste, or overzealous ambition. We have to learn to recognise that voice and listen. It is rarely wrong.

Wisdom is something that I can only allude to in a book. I can inspire you to search for it with my words, but I cannot teach it to you, not even in a decade of personal tuition. It is something you have to learn for yourself. Wisdom is the final product of processed experience.

The Buddha always warned that the writings were not the way—they only lead to the way. He said that his way would not, could not, and should not, be *your* way. Your way is yours, and yours alone. The more experience you gain, especially of the type that is dangerous and takes you over the edges of your comfort, the more wisdom you will gleam.

Wisdom is not something you can buy ready-mixed and ready to bake, or take off the shelf like a one-size-fits-all suit. It is also not something you can pick from the best-seller shelf at Waterstones, or borrow second-hand from an Oriental spiritual mystic. Your wisdom is yours, no one else's. It will be entirely unique, something that develops from, by, and out of your life experience, and something that will continue to develop as long as you continue to experience.

Why would you want it to be otherwise? Why be a clone? There are billions of them out there already, mere machines trying their hardest to look and be like all the other machines. They borrow quotes and walk through life like a watered down same-as-everyone-else High Street brand.

This should be below your game. This *is* below your game. You should be excited about this. It means that what you develop will be a one-off original. No one else in the world will have it. If you are courageous enough to develop and finesse your wisdom, it will take you anywhere. And, of course, your uniqueness will shine like a bright star, and people will traverse the globe to touch the very original hand of your experience. That, my friends, is worth getting up in the morning for.

» Warrior Practices

In this chapter I would like to encourage you to start a steady regime of daily physical training in order to develop mastery over your body. Too many people are trying to understand the mysterious before they master the material. A basic foundation of good physical, physiological, and psychological control is the vital starting point to every warrior journey. This enables you to master your vehicle and gain a tolerance for discomfort. It will also help you win a healthy balance in your body and in your life.

If you want to build a tower block that goes high into the sky, you need to start by digging a very deep and very wide foundation. It is no good trying to build a tower block on the foundation of your old semi. In martial arts training, a strong core system like karate or judo, wrestling or boxing, would act as a powerful foundation. On top of that kind of base, you can build pretty much anything you want.

So if it is a martial art that you choose as a warrior-base, any of these systems would suffice, according to your personality and body type. I started with Gung fu, then went into Japanese Shotokan. I trained in these arts for many years, using the very hard training as a foundation for my body, mind, and spirit.

Later I extended these arts by going heavily into judo and wrestling, Thai boxing, and Western boxing, I even studied weaponry as a natural extension of my hands. I delved into every dirty corner of these arts, challenging myself to master all the areas that scared me. The areas that scared me most were the places you would find me.

In martial arts, I found my burn quickly, and I stayed in it long. This gave me maximum growth in the minimum time. I then took those skills into the world and placed them, and my psyche, under pressure. I worked in a very unforgiving employ: the doors.

I became a bouncer for a decade, to see if the skills I had learned would work under pressure. I wanted to see if my spirit would hold up under extreme scrutiny of an environ that punished minor mistakes with a visit to the hospital, and major errors with a marble slab and a toe tag. Four of my friends were murdered during my time as a doorman. I dove-tailed and balanced this training and pressure testing with a study of psychology, physiology, and psychiatry. I wanted to know what made me tick, and what I could do to improve my game.

Later still, when I had exhausted more physical martial arts than you can shake a stick at, I allowed my study to spill from the base physical over to the metaphysical. Here is where violent encounters are avoided at the level of thought, and whole realities are built and burnt from the inside out. More about his later in the book.

There are a million different methods of physical training out there that can help you in your quest for sovereignty of the self. Your job at this stage is to listen to your bodily instinct and find the one or ones that are right for you.

Often you find the right method of training by simply ploughing through a plethora of the wrong ones first. If you are smart, you will lean into the sharp edges and go for the training that scares you most. In martial arts I'd go for judo, wrestling, boxing and Thai—if time permits, all of them. A good martial artist should be savvy in every range. These systems are honest and they are real. There is no hiding place here. The growth is fast and it is guaranteed. With any of the other systems that I have looked at, there is very little brand consistency. You can get one club that is amazing, and another in the same system that is dire.

For instance, in judo, wrestling or boxing, you could go pretty much anywhere and almost guarantee a hardy class. Go into other systems if you like and see how it feels, but for fast-track control of the body through martial arts, these are my top four.

As a rule of thumb with a martial art remember this: If it does not scare you, you are in the wrong place. This is martial art, an art that is designed for war. If it does not scare the shit out of you, it is not going to prepare you for anything. You might as well take up dance for all the good it will do you. When you train in your fear, you train on the fast track.

Weight training, running, cycling, and athletics are all good, and, to be honest, you can gain control of the physical body through most of them. If you start hitting marathons and hill training, it starts to spill into the psychological, which will develop mental hardiness. But if you really want to learn control of the psychological elements, you can't beat a good base system of martial arts.

» Life Inventory

I would also like to encourage you at this point to write down an honest inventory of your life. Write down your fears and aspirations, so you can gradually dissolve the areas that are holding you back, and move you towards your warrior life. In this area, you need to look at everything from your job to your relationships, from where you live, to how you live.

To be a warrior you need to collect power, or more specifically, you need to reconnect to the power that is already in you. (More on this in the next chapter). To do this, you need to look at all the areas in your life that disempower you.

Most people I meet are married to the wrong person, living in the wrong house, working in the wrong job, and driving the wrong car. Often they are living entirely the wrong life. All of these things can be changed. They are all within your power.

Be completely frank with yourself, and bravely write down all the difficult things you would like to improve. Maybe you are with the right partner, but somewhere along the line one of you has gotten lost. With honesty, courage, and positive change, you can bring that balance back.

Perhaps your job is not fulfilling. Change it for one that is, or at least improve the conditions of the one you are presently in. So many people work in jobs they can't stand, but they don't change them because change is uncomfortable. This chapter is all about seeking a difficult life. Write the inventory and completely re-shape your life so that it better suits your aspirations. Remember, you haven't got long. Your stay on this planet is a short, blink of an eye in terms of a universe unfolding. Make good of the time you have now.

I visited a factory owned by a friend recently while doing research on a TV project. My friend pointed out one particular guy who was working at an automated lathe, one of those product line machines that does the job of five men. Once the operator set it up, all that was needed was to collect/count the finished jobs at the other end.

I watched that man with some fascination as he stood there collecting and counting machine parts, obviously watching the clock, and hoping that break time and home time would come soon. It was mind numbingly boring.

My friend explained to me that the lathe operator in question was a skilled man. This job was below his potential. Yet every time he considered taking on a more challenging job with a fatter wage packet, he began to stress. And every time the manger suggested that he apply for a promotion with more money, he stressed.

So he stays where he is, dying slowly, atrophy in action. A machine operating another machine, and all because he is too scared to be uncomfortable.

I know the feeling well. I spent my first 30 years on this spinning planet doing exactly the same thing. It doesn't need to be like that. When you live like a warrior, all things become possible. Nothing is out of your reach.

Often when you write a list like this, you find that your fears and your aspirations are one and the same. People fear the things they most desire. They fear success. Often this is not immediately clear or obvious on the surface. Sometimes it is not until we are right on top of the realisation of our goals that we see how scary they really are. That is one of the reasons I like to get people to write a list in the first place.

Some people are too scared to admit their fears, which in and of itself is a fear. They are also frightened to write down their dreams and aspirations. Seeing the paper and ink version of a goal is the very first physical manifestation of it. Writing it down will also announce the beginning of your quest to make your dream a reality. It will beg lots of questions: How? Why? Where? When?

Seeing a goal on paper will demand that you unearth a purpose that is strong enough to carry that dream to reality. And more than anything else, seeing that dream in black and white will force you to answer one vital question: How much do I want it?'

Let *me* ask you here and now, 'how much *do* you want it?' The manifestation of our desires always asks a lot. It will demand full immersion, and not many people are prepared to pay the price.

This fear of success is called the Jonah Complex. In our mind's eye we revel in the things we know we can achieve, and at the same time, we recoil with terror at the very thought of realising them. This is because achieving our wildest dreams means change, and change scares us more than the sabre-toothed tiger of antiquity.

We come back to discomfort again.

Discomfort is a given on this journey. Converting our God-given energy into matter is an intrinsically uncomfortable process. At this very moment I am converting energy though my body and onto the computer screen, and every second of it is uncomfortable. Physically, it is uncomfortable to sit for hours at a computer. Mentally, it hurts to make the conversion from thought to page. And spiritually, it is a continual battle to turn up day after day to make my energy into a book.

I've been writing books for 20 years now and I know how to do it. I know how to make the conversion—but it still hurts. I still get apprehension (and excitement and fear), before every new project.

In a few minutes time I am going for a run with my wife, Sharon, as part of my daily training session. I will convert energy to make the run a reality, and it will hurt as it always hurts. But here's the point: I love it. I am not only comfortable with the creation of pain, I love and thrive on the creation of pain.

I understand that I have access to an infinite amount of energy, and everything in the material world is created by that energy. I have the same access to that energy as Bill Gates, the same access as Bruce Lee, the same access as Mahatma Ghandi, and the same access as Steve Jobs. I can create anything I want with it, provided I am prepared to endure the creative burn that is the necessary precursor to any manifestation.

So write a list of your fears. Write a list of your goals or dreams. Make it extensive, make it expansive, and be as comprehensive as possible. It is vital that you are brutally honest. You don't have to show anyone the list if you don't want to, but you must be honest with yourself.

The very act of writing a list takes courage—so write it.

When you're done, look at the list, study the list, and make a vow to yourself here and now to go over the list on a daily basis. This will help you start erasing your fears and begin to make your dreams a reality. As I said, usually the two lists will cross because they are intrinsically linked. As you erase your fear, you will be free to realise you desire.

You will find when you write down your fears and aspirations, and you start—however slowly—to work on them, there will be a huge change in dynamic. You will no longer be the person that is going to erase your fears, you will actually be *doing* it. And you will no longer be that person who is always talking about achieving his or her goals. You will actually be in the process of doing it.

This one small act will make all the difference, as you reap confidence from your action. That confidence is real, and is a great equity that you can grow. Each time you face a fear or act on your goal, you will add to that confidence-equity, and it will expand.

And the exciting thing is, your potential for growth is limitless. You are a bundle of infinite possibilities. These potentials have always been there, and they will always be there. They just need a warrior mentality to make them a reality.

Chapter summary:

This chapter is about searching for the road less travelled and taking it. Everyone that seeks an easy life ultimately ends up with an unsatisfying existence. The warrior turns the world on it head and looks for the anti-intuitive truths, often hidden in plain sight. In this case, you will find expansion only by courting difficulty.

Chapter Two

†

A Warrior...
Seeks Self-Mastery

As Tolstoy once said, if you want to change the world, you have to start by changing yourself. Most people have no sense of their own potential or their own power. They have no idea how to garner it, how to hold it, or how to distribute it so that it is a creative force for good.

Instead, most people focus on trying to obtain their power through material acquisition and influence. These are not the powers that a warrior seeks—they are ephemeral and can be taken away by the wheel of fortune at any time. The warrior looks instead toward real power, a power that is already in him waiting to be discovered and developed.

I alluded to this in the last chapter, and in essence, sovereignty over the self is what this book is all about. It is, in fact, what life is all about. All the spiritual tomes concur. The

Testament, The Holy Quran, the Bhagavad-Gita, the Guru Granthe Sahib—all encourage and promote mastery over the self, sovereignty over the corporeal.

When Nelson Mandela was in prison on Robin Island for 30 years, he said there were many days when he was on his knees, unable to carry on. But he continued to recite a poem over and over for the entire term of his imprisonment. Just a few lines and verses from *Invictus*, written by William Ernest Henley some 100 years before, kept this great man alive. The last four lines of the poem are what inspired Mandela most:

It matters not how straight the gate
How charged with punishment the scroll,
I am a master of my fate,
I am the captain of my soul.

This is the essence of self sovereignty. It is a right we all have a claim to, yet it is a power that few call forward. When a person does call it forward and own it, mountains move, seas part, the world stands up and listens.

Mandela had it. Gandhi found it. And Mother Teresa of Calcutta was drenched in it. It would be easy to see these people as extraordinary members of our species, but I would argue differently. They are very ordinary members of this beautiful species that were called to action, and they did extraordinary things.

That access is denied to no one. It is available to all. You just have to have the courage to collect on it. Courage is not something you can grow in a Petri dish. It is not a commodity that you can get on a buy-two-get-one-free special at Sainsbury's. You have to take yourself out into the world and earn it.

The Mexican Shamans actually sought out difficult situations in their life, because they understood that is where all the power is. They collected power. How exciting, to be a collector of power. 'What are you doing today?' 'Actually, I am going out to hunt down my fears so that I can collect some power.' Now that is what warriorship is all about. Hunting fear. Tracking down your darkest, direst terrors and having it out with them.

The poet Rumi called the process Night Travelling, and said that the moon shone for those who embraced their fears. The more difficult the situation, the more power it contains. Not that the situation itself actually holds power, of course. Rather, the situation confronted and overcome, triggers the power that is already latent in us, waiting to be released.

This is what I said earlier about changing perspective. A

body-builder knows that the power he seeks is in the burn. That is why he happily chases the burn and stays in the burn and learns to love the burn. He does not see, think of, or talk about the burn as an unbearable pain. He sees it only as a catalyst for growth.

The same applies in all areas. Business expands when you have the courage to go to that place of discomfort. Health is enhanced greatly by people that engage everyday in 'uncomfortable' exercise. And relationships thrive when couples have honest and open (and uncomfortable) discussions with each other. I see so many marriages flounder because the husband or the wife does not have the courage to openly talk about an element of the relationship with which they are unhappy. And as we should all know, we are only as sick as our secrets.

When you change perspective everything that happens to you can be turned to the good.

So where does sovereignty start? What does sovereignty involve?

Let me tell you where it starts with me. I live my whole life from the inspiration of one verse from the Bhagavad-Gita:

Lift the self by the self;
Never let the self droop down;

The self is the self's only friend;

The self is the self's only enemy.

I love that, don't you? It is not your wife's fault. It is not your mum and dad's fault. It is not the fault of society or the government. There is no conspiracy against you. There are no people sitting is a room trying to make your life difficult. Thinking these thoughts disempowers you because it means that until *they* change, *you* can't change.

What I have learned and what I know is this: The power is all with you. In fact, it has always been in you. It is yours. The lottery, the X factor, the fortune, the good health, the beautiful mate—they are all in you just waiting to happen.

But they are unlikely to happen if you are looking outside of yourself for power. There is no power out there other than the power that you create.

Let me tell you about this girl I met recently. Powerful girl—or so she thinks. She heads what is deemed a powerful organization, and she has lunch with seemingly powerful people at what she calls *power lunches*. She draws what some might consider a powerful amount of money in her monthly wage packet, and she has been known to dally with members of Parliament, where the seat of power has had to be expanded because so many of the powerful men and women in the House have gotten so powerfully fat.

And yet, when you stand with her, she is not present. Never. Well, unless of course, she thinks there might be some influence in being seen with you.

I have to stipulate here that she is a lovely girl. There is absolutely nothing to dislike about her. But she has no power. None at all. In fact, I have yet to meet a person with less power. She whispers, *very powerful,* when talking about the people she meets, as though saying it aloud might create a leakage, or others might steal what is rightly hers. Those people have no power either. They have no power because they are looking for power in all the wrong places.

People say to me, *it's who you know.* I disagree. There is no real power in who you know. The power is in what you do, and what you do triggers your own personal supply of power.

Others say, *it's the awards you win.* Again, not true. There is no real power in awards, in money, or in influence. These things are flavours, and they come and they go. If you rely on them for power then your power is not really yours. When you have real power, the power over yourself, it will not be taken away by condition or contrition, or by Boethius' spinning wheel of fortune.

Warriors do not look for power on coattails. They do not look for power from other people. The do not consider their job powerful or otherwise. If they did, then their power would be temporary, and a warrior's power is anything but temporary.

A warrior has to fight demons to get power, but once acquired, it is never lost. He does not look for power in money; there is no sustainable power in money in and of itself. Money is a good organizer. It can buy things. But one of the things it cannot purchase is real power. Even if it says 'contains power' on the packet, take it from me, it contains no power whatsoever.

The power base of the warrior is control of palate: What he eats, drinks, ingests, reads, listens to and is influenced by. This is the start.

As I said earlier, there is no use trying to master the universe when you are still overweight and/or addicted. There is much denial on the planet at the moment, with lots of people looking for lots of power in all the wrong places. They are dangerously unhealthy because of their daily habits and addictions, but still feel as though the universe is there for the taking. It is of course, but not before you get the basics right.

We had a rule in weightlifting: Don't load up a man's bar with more weight if he can't handle the weight he is already pushing.

My friend was at an NLP seminar recently with two of the top teachers in the business. He was among a class full of people who had spent a large wad of money to hear these two powerful practitioners speak. One of the men instructing is a pioneer in NLP, and has traversed the globe searching for power. By all accounts he is a nice man. However, both of the instructors were clinically obese, between them carrying about 10 stone of waste on their bodies. Additionally, they both had a nicotine addiction, even though they were in denial about it. Think about it. This is supposedly the most powerful system in the world for self-change, and yet the two leading practitioners were unable to make it work on themselves. It couldn't even break them free from denial.

Basics first. Master what you eat, master what you drink, and monitor your influences closely. Most of what you watch on TV and read in the newspapers is highly subjective. I am not saying the news is not true. I am saying it is not balanced or objective. I know from my contacts in journalism that reporters are sent out to find juicy (negative) stories that will sell the front of a newspaper. The juicier the better. Most days, people are fed a diet of junk-food information that does nothing to empower. It is, in fact, disempowering.

If you hear from the media several times a day that the economic sky is going to fall at any minute, how do you think the news is going to affect you? Your whole reality is based largely on what you ingest on a daily basis. If that reality is not empowering, then you need to change what you take in.

To master the self you have to be in charge of the self, and that means recognizing that what you put in is what you get out. You are literally what you eat, what you drink, what you watch on television, and who you are influenced by. Everything that enters your body though your mouth, through your ears, through your eyes, and through your touch becomes the eco-structure that is you. Information in its many forms enters your body, and immediately becomes chemical and then flesh. It becomes you. So changing these things for the better is an essential first step.

Gandhi started initially by mastering himself through palate. He said that once you control palate, all the other senses fall into line. Once you control the senses, you control yourself. And when you control yourself, you literally control the whole world.

This is a method that took this once-anonymous man from

obscurity to the world stage. He has more than 350 million followers—all through mastery of the self.

With food, I recommend what the Buddhists call the middle way. This is a tricky balance of not-too-much food and not-too-little. Let your body tell you where that middle place is. Obviously, if you are overweight you are eating too much. Issues with cholesterol and blood pressure indicate a balance has not yet been found.

Correct eating can cure a plethora of ills. Over consumption of the wrong food is connected to many ailments. One of the main areas of concern is that excessive eating can have a detrimental effect on the adrenal glands and make you more susceptible to stress. As you are probably aware, stress is a killer that releases all sorts of hormones into the body for fight or flight. These can act as a caustic to the smooth internal muscles in the heart, the lungs, the intestines, etc. Stress is even linked to problems in the brain, where it is thought to attack neurotransmitters vital for mental health.

The key for me is light eating and smaller portions. This strategy places less stress on digestion which is where a lot of our energy is lost. Plenty of fruits and vegetables are vital. I eat very little meat, but when I do, I usually stick to white meat and fish. I also avoid the obvious excesses of sugar, salt, and pastries. Additionally, I haven't consumed alcohol for 10 years.

Some people can manage to drink moderately. Most do not, and are probably underestimating the amount they consume.

One of my friends, heavily in denial about his lifestyle, has even developed the habit of re-naming his excess. He now calls it *too much partying*. It is apparently more acceptable and easier to say that he is partying too much, than it is to say *I'm getting pissed too often, and it is threatening my life.*

» Kill your addictions.

Food, of course, is a major addiction for many people. It is not an *obvious* addiction however, as many addicts may be unaware they have an issue. We are so accustomed to seeing the addiction label attached to drugs and alcohol that the more obvious—and often more dangerous—addictions, like food and *people-pleasing*, continue to tick away in the background unnoticed.

Understanding food and the issues it can cause should be a priority. In addition to being our main source of energy, it is what I call, the *first influence*. You have probably heard a million times that you are what you eat, a phrase so common that it no longer registers. People still eat like a truck driver and wonder why they do not get an F-1 performance out of their vehicle. Control of your food intake is paramount. It is the very basis of who we are. If you put diesel oil into your unleaded car would you be surprised when it breaks down halfway up the street? Probably not. So why be surprised when your body fails after eating shit, or drinking poison, or listening to crap?

Most people do this every day of their lives. They have no control over their food intake, and yet they sit and talk about going on great adventures and mastering the universe. *If you want to change the universe, start by changing yourself.* One of the great things about palate control and mastering your food intake is that you will start to feel less anxiety and fear. Obstacles that are blocking your path from a successful warrior lifestyle will also dissolve, leaving you a clear path to anywhere and a direct route to everywhere.

This is because wrong-eating triggers the adrenals. Our overeating is also a manifestation of us feeding our shadows, our fears, our insecurities, and our limitations. Our small thinking is fed by our addictions (see *Hunting the Shadow*). When this happens, all our power is being swallowed up by overfed shadows that become obese inside us.

You need to make your body inhospitable for shadows. You need to make your body so balanced that there is not a single corner of your being where these shady characters can hide.

Shadows love nothing more than a pornographic body. There are a million places in a body of excess for these scavengers to squat. They like dirty bodies, fat bodies, greedy bodies. They love bodies that do not move much or train. Lazy, inert bodies are their favourite nesting place. The more you open the door to them by opening yourself to easy addiction, the more shadows will inhabit you. If you open the door to one addiction, you open the door to all addictions.

When I worked as a nightclub bouncer in Coventry, we had a strict rule: No undesirables allowed in the club. None. Not ever. We enforced this rule with an iron hand. We kept the trouble away by keeping a strong front door. In other words, we made sure that there was strength—three top doormen—at the entrance to the club. These had to be courageous men who were not afraid to defend the front door with their very lives. We learned early and we learned well that if you let one undesirable into the club, you sent out an invitation to all the undesirables in the city. Once they were inside, you had a hell of a battle on your hands to get them out again. This could be a battle you were not guaranteed to win. Many of the weaker doors in the city were afraid to stop the gangsters at the door. They let them in, hoping to buy favour with some of the stronger, darker forces. It didn't work. Once they allowed the gangsters in, the club belonged to the gangsters. It became their domain. This is the same with addictions. Let them through the front door at your peril. You let one through, you let all through.

All addictions are controlling and disempowering. For instance, once you allow sexual pornography into your mind, how hard is it to get it back out again? You find yourself wanting more and more until it is all you think about. You then find yourself looking for any opportunity to access the filth on the World Wide Web. Your wife nips out shopping, you're on the web. She goes to bed early, you're sneaking onto the web. You might be innocently browsing the Internet for some legitimate information, when suddenly, seemingly against your own will and better judgment, you find yourself excited and hitting the porn sites. You are no longer in charge. Your addiction is in charge.

It is the same with food, the same with drugs, and the same with any addiction. The addiction talks to you, subtly at first, telling you that *a little bit of what you fancy will do you good. Who is it hurting anyway? You've had a hard day, a hard week, a hard life. You deserve a little treat. Do it one more time and then stop. Or, who's going to know anyway?*

Later, when the addiction takes over, it is less subtle. In fact it becomes overt, aggressive, and demanding. It is prepared to fight to the death to defend its rights, happy to lose everything to have its fix, adamant despite all the best advise (medical and otherwise) that it will have what it wants.

I have friends and family members who've lost everything—ultimately their own lives—to defend their addiction. One told me violently to back off when I mentioned that he was drinking too much. *I've earned the right to have a drink,* he told me. *I worked all my life to have a drink.*

Another friend, dying from alcohol, complained to me that she *hardly drank at all,* and yet her family was still against her. *Apparently,* she said to me, pissed and arrogant and angry, *I'm the one in the family with a drink problem.*

No, actually she was the one in the family with a *denial* problem. Huge denial. Denial so dense that a whole extended family of love could not get through to her.

Addictions are insidious, cunning, and deadly. Too much drinking is not *too much partying.* It is too much denial. Too much eating is not *an issue*—it is a fucking killer. Sexual pornography is not *natural*. It is an inhabiting demon that is taking over your life. If you don't think so, try and get rid of it, and see how it fights and claws for its very life.

Drugs are not *recreational*. That's a crap word used by the weak-minded who are trying to rationalize indulging in a mass addiction. They are not OK in moderation, because moderation is simply a loss leader making way for the big guns that are looking for a fleshy squat.

Addictions are either dead or they are deadly. You cannot flirt with them and come out ahead. But here is the thing. Like vampires, they cannot cross your threshold unless you invite them in. So do not invite them in. If they are already in, start the starvation process immediately. If you stop feeding them, they will eventually die. It is a universal law. What we pay attention to will grow. What we take attention away from will atrophy.

So get started now. Make your body an inhospitable environ. Make it impossibly uncomfortable for addictions to hang around. Make yourself a hard target for future addiction by being on the lookout at all times. Keep a strong front door, and beat away the gangsters at the entrance to the club.

This is how a warrior lives. He is not a warrior just because he calls himself a warrior. If you are still full of addictions you are weak. Call yourself a puppet, but do not pretend that you are a warrior. Do not dare call yourself powerful, even if your job title, or your bank balance, or your benching record suggests otherwise. In the quiet of night, when everyone else has gone to bed and you are alone, have a good look at yourself in the mirror... *you know* what you are.

If you don't like the image looking back at you, change it. Change it *now*.

The exciting bit, as I mentioned before, is that the moment we stop feeding our addictions, the shadows atrophy and die. We get access to our power again, and we get access to our body again. We are no longer possessed.

Getting a fit body and being in shape are small by-products compared to the real gains we get when we master ourselves by murdering our addictions.

I will not patronize you with lists of food you should and should not eat. There are a million programs on TV about healthy eating and a plethora of books that tell you what you already know. When you fully commit to regaining your power by mastering your eating, you will automatically know what to eat and what to leave in the bin. As I have already said, the main thing from my experience is to eat light. Small portions. Even better, small and often. Six small meals a day will keep your energy levels high. Eating light (meaning very little, if any, red meat) is also a great deterrent against ill health. Many of our ills are triggered by wrong eating. As mentioned earlier, overeating has an enormous detrimental effect on your whole system. My wife and I tend to share meals, so we eat perhaps half as much as a normal person. This takes a lot of strain off digestion, which uses copious amounts of energy to digest excess food, and leaves vastly more energy.

The philosopher Gurdjieffe believed that each of us, when balanced, should have enough energy and power to create a livelihood for 21 people or more. Most people are unable to adequately create a livelihood even for themselves and their family, let alone 20 others. We have access to a tremendous amount of power, but it takes a warrior to access and deliver it. Some people who are not balanced can still create at this level, but it is usually to the detriment of their health, their relationships, or both.

» Warrior Practices:

The practice for this chapter has already been alluded to in the chapter itself. I invite you to write an inventory of all the habits and addictions you are aware of. Be as honest and as forthright as you can.

Start with the food and drink.

Write down the food you eat, and how you could improve your eating habits. If you are overweight, your body is already indicating that you are eating too much. Start by cutting down the portion sizes. This is uncomfortable to start with, but remember please what I said earlier about changing perception. When you are working with anabolic discomfort, you are collecting power. So every time you feel uncomfortable and the discomfort bothers you, remind yourself of this. You are not giving anything up, you are escaping. You are not making your life miserable, you are investing in a happy, healthy, and powerful future. The part of you that feels unhappy and uncomfortable is the shadow that your addiction is feeding. You are kicking out squatters, and they are acting up. That is all. You are not losing pleasure, you are gaining power.

In the long run, your pleasure will multiply. As you get into it more and more, you will receive increasing amounts of pleasure out of not being addicted. You will find it is a real high, and involves much more pleasure than you ever got out of being an addict. There are no side effects from being free from addiction. As the shadows die and you regain control of your body, you will gain more and more access to the natural powers around you. And whilst you will undoubtedly lose friends (other addicts), when you kill your shadows, you will find yourself flying in an entirely different frequency. In this place you will make more friends, better friends.

Take a look at your other daily intakes. No need to write these down, just observe them. Think about what you read, what you watch on TV, and what you listen to on the radio. Take into account the conversations you have and the company you keep.

How do they make you feel?

If you are reading, watching, listening to, and being around negative media constantly, then that is what you are ultimately going to be. The information we take in every day and process becomes our reality. Most of the information being doled out by the popular media is of a pornographic nature. In other words, it is excessively negative.

This does not serve you. You don't need to judge it, be angry at it, attack it, or even necessarily understand why it's like it is. Just know it is not serving you and change it. You need to make better choices. The fact that you are reading a book about living like a warrior suggests to me that you are already making better choices. So now make *more* better choices. Change newspapers if the one you are reading is sensational. Instead, read words that are more inspiring, or at least, words that are more objective. Read articles that motivate you toward more than the lottery and X Factor on the TV. You are your own lottery. You already have the X Factor.

If the company you keep does not improve your day, change the company you keep. You don't have to make any big announcements about this, just be brutally honest with yourself. If the people you are around are just an extension of the tabloid newspapers, gradually move away from them and gravitate towards people at a higher frequency.

As you develop your centre by changing your daily habits, you may find that this is happening anyway. You will probably have already found yourself getting increasingly uncomfortable around certain people and in certain social situations. Don't resist this. It is a natural progression upwards. Of course, if it is close family members, your wife or husband, it can be more difficult. The worst thing you can do is try to convert them to your new way of thinking. People always resist when you evangelize. Just work on yourself. Be diligent, get your food right, kill your bad habits, stop taking in anything that feeds your bad habits, and you will start to shine.

When this happens, you'll find that the people closest to you will want to shine too, and they will follow you. They will want what you have. This is where you have to have faith in the process. When you change, everything around you will change—that is certain.

As I said earlier, change can be scary for people. But if you expect it, as you will now, it will not be quite so daunting.

Change is inevitable. It is a constant. Everything is changing all the time. Change is uncomfortable, but discomfort is where the warrior collects his power. You are living like a warrior, so your perception is different from everyone else's. You like discomfort. You understand that the challenge will develop new and powerful aspects of yourself that you did not even know existed.

Even better, people will feel your new-found power. When you walk into a room there will be a trail of power following. People will be drawn to you. The old you will be replaced by a shiny new model, one that has control of his or her life. You will be a person that can walk out of the house on any given day and think, *Shall I turn right today or shall I turn left? Shall I got forward or shall I have a day at home?* There will no longer be any situation that will imprison you. You are in charge of your incarnation. And you will do whatever you want with it.

This new power is a certainty. It is a given. From this power, you will get more and more power. But there is an obvious danger. People often misuse their position. A very big part of living a warrior life is making sure you do not use your power to hurt anyone, that you only use your potency for the good. This might sound a little corny, but it needs to be said. Power exerted in the wrong way always damages. It can damage you if you mishandle it, and it can damage the people around you. I have found that unannounced power is the most potent kind. Just do what you do, be aware of what you do, and adjust what you do if it is too much for other people. Allow yourself a little time to adjust to your new levels of power. Above all be gentle. That is the most powerful thing you can ever do. It takes great strength of character.

Chapter Summary:

This chapter is about mastering the self, initially through palate. All the power you will ever need can be accessed through the physical, but not until the physical is brought under the control of the will.

Chapter Three

†

A WARRIOR IS...
GENTLE.

There is a tendency to believe that being a warrior means you have to become war-like and hurt people. Actually, the opposite is true. The seasoned warrior hurts no one. He has mastered himself, and his confidence enables him to practice the art of gentleness even in the midst of aggression. As the Taoist monk Pao Piao Tse said, *the preeminent scholar can obtain Toa even in the battlefield.*

When you are supremely confident and you understand yourself and others, you realise that violence, wherever it is directed, is futile. It always rebounds on itself. A warrior recognises that everything is connected, and that to harm another ultimately means to harm one's self. This may sound like sickly sweet spirituality, but when you are looking at life from my perspective you realize that it is a hugely powerful spiritual stance. There is nothing more attractive in my eyes than someone who has tremendous power and chooses to use it to promote gentleness.

Leo Tolstoy, the preeminent Russian novelist was one such man. He spent his whole life promoting peace, and was instrumental in developing the passive resistance movement, a philosophy later embraced and employed with incredible success by Mahatma Gandhi and Martin Luther King. Gandhi actually brought the British Empire to its knees using non-violent marches and protests. He literally changed the course of history without ever once throwing a punch or firing a bullet in anger.

Having been a man of aggression myself for almost a decade, I can attest to the futility of violence. I can also stand testament to the power it takes to be gentle when you have the ability to hurt—even kill—to get your own way.

I have spent my entire life studying the killing techniques of myriad martial arts, from Chinese Gung Fu right through to Greco Roman wrestling. I have the ability to kill a man dead in 20 different ways using only my bare hands as weapons. I have dropped many a foe on the violent nightclub doors of my city, and I have to tell you that it sickened me.

I found no power in hurting others, none at all. And like Soul on the road to Damascus, I had my moment of clarity. I saw at once how heinous and self-defeating violence is, and I immediately renounced it as a means of communication. I instead focused on developing skills in articulation, and learned a little over-the-table negotiation.

Later still, when delving into the world of metaphysics, I realized that with powerful and positive thinking, I could avoid aggressive situations by simply not creating the aggressive situations in the first place. After much soul searching and honest introspection, I realized that I had been creating my own reality. Up until that point my reality was one of aggression and violence. I talked about violence. I wrote about violence. I watched violence on the television, and read about it every day in the newspapers. I carried weapons of violence—the most dangerous of which were my ill-schooled intellect and my badly directed intent. In fact, every room of my house contained at least one weapon, right down to the very smallest room. My thinking was in a constant cycle of three-dimensional violence. Because I lived and breathed it, I created violence copiously in my reality.

The moment I realized this, I made the necessary and uncomfortable changes. Every negative was replaced with a positive. Every weapon was binned and its space taken up by a book. I started watching, reading about, and talking about creativity. Like a large ocean liner, my turn-around was slow, but it was definite and defined. Once the changes were in place, I started to practice the art of gentleness. Violence was no longer in my armory. It was a mode of badinage that I now considered to be below my game. I physically practiced gentleness in my everyday life. When I saw or sensed or felt aggression or violence, I worked on dissolving it before it had any chance to grow and expand.

This tactic takes confidence of course, but the reward for practicing confidence is more confidence. The more you hone it the better you get. I actively practiced avoiding aggressive situations. If I saw a scenario arising I would escape it. If it came on top of me and escape was not an option, then I would use verbal dissuasion, talk the situation down. I also started to work with *frequency*. I recognized that violence in all its forms is a low-frequency activity. Trying to solve violence with more violence is like adding more black to try to get rid of black.

This made me work in higher frequencies, like humour, understanding, intelligence, compassion, and ultimately, love. Through practice, I discovered that aggression could be dissolved inside and outside if I accessed and held the higher frequency of love. Not easy I have to say, especially when you consider that aggression in others tends to automatically trigger aggression or fear in us, pulling anyone in the vicinity into the same low bandwidth.

I have knocked many people unconscious in my life, and I have damaged, nearly killed, many more. But it was not an intelligent means of discourse, and I found that for every aggressor I put down, another two aggressors would rise in his place. The more aggression I employed, the more aggression I attracted—until my life was nothing but wall-to-wall violence. I could not move for the stuff, yet I learned a very exciting lesson, a universal law. What you pay attention to grows; what you take attention away from will atrophy. Give something a copious amount of attention and it will expand copiously. Take all the attention away from something and it will die just as surely as a plant withers away without light.

Gentleness is an art that needs practice. It needs attention. Practice a little bit and you will get a little bit good at it. Make it your life's work and you will become a master of gentleness. Now *that* is an art worth learning.

I have few gentle heroes, but my heads on favourite is a

man called George Hackenschmidt. He was a master of catch wrestling and world champion weightlifter in the early part of the 1900s. An incredible athlete, he was so popular that he brought London to a log-jam every time he held a bout of wrestling there. He once fought the American champion, Karl Gotch, in Gorky Park, USA, and attracted 50,000 paying fans. He was the Cassius Clay of his day. He was wined and dined by royalty, and was known to have conversed with the great thinkers of the day, including George Bernard Shaw.

What I loved about Hack (as he was known), was that he was not just a perfect physical specimen that could snap you in half with his bare hands, he was also a great intellect. He could speak five languages, he wrote and published books, and he was legendary for his gentleness. If reporters wanted to interview him, he'd take them to lunch at his expense. If adoring fans wanted an autograph, he would always oblige, taking time out to encourage them with their training or with their life.

Once, when he alighted from a train on one of his many visits to a northern city in England, he was greeted by hundreds of fans. All the local celebrities of the day were there, ready to show him the freedom and hospitality of their city. On the platform, buried behind a glut of cheering bodies, he noticed a young, ailing lad who was desperately trying to get a glimpse of Hack. The great wrestler waded through the crowd and made his way over to the lad who was *awestruck* to be within touching distance of his hero.

When Hack crouched down, he could see the boy was ailing and weak, so he spent a few minutes talking with him. He encouraged him to train, to get fit and strong, and perhaps one day become a champion lifter like him.

If I can do it, Hack told him, *then you can do it too.* Hack understood the power of his position, and he used it to great effect. The locals were stunned by the gentleness of this legendary character. Many years later, fuelled by Hack's love and advice, that young boy went on to become a world champion himself, beating all the lifting records previously set. By investing a few minutes of his time and some kind words, Hack had helped turn this small boy into a champion.

For Nelson Mandela it took many long years of imprisonment for him to find the power of gentleness. When he was finally released after 30 years, the very first thing he did was forgive the people that had put him there. He didn't do it because he was trying to be a great bloke, or because he was trying to impress. He forgave them because he knew that forgiveness was the most powerful weapon he had. In his early years he had tried violence and terrorism, the traditional warrior fare. It did not work. It just added to his problems and the problems of his beloved country. He was not about to make the same mistake again. Many of his followers were angry at his stance, not wanting him to forgive his captors. They thought it was a weak response to a situation that needed some steel. Others thought that the long and debilitating prison sentence had weakened Mandela, and that he had become soft. Some were outraged, seeing his forgiveness as a license for his South African captors to continue with their repressive regime.

What Mandela knew, and what I have learned from my own life, is that forgiveness is actually a metaphysical force, possessing the power of a thousand armies.

In one of his many famous speeches as president of South Africa, Mandela told his fellow countrymen that the time for violence was over. There would be no more violence. He had witnessed firsthand the futility of it, and had learned it was a weak foundation on which to build a country—just as it is a weak foundation on which to build a life. He is now known throughout the world as one of the most powerful leaders in the history of our species. And his leadership is built on gentleness.

Gentleness is powerful because its language is love, and its frequency is love. Love is a force that can move mountains.

A warrior seeks to be gentle in all that he does. If he is not gentle, then he is not a warrior. To be a warrior means to be completely secure in yourself, supremely confident in your abilities, certain about who you are, at ease with what you are, and attached to your own power with immediate access to the infinite universal power. Violence is not the language of the warrior. It is the language of insecurity and fear, and the parley of the weak. It may have been a stage of the warrior's journey, but it is not who or where he is now.

If there are any areas of your life that remain aggressive or violent, know that they need to be rooted out and dissolved.

In my opinion, *Alice in Wonderland,* is one of the best books on metaphysics ever written. In it, the White Queen rules with love and gentleness, whilst the Red Queen rules with fear and hate. In the film (2010 version) and in the book, it becomes immediately clear, even to the hard of thinking, that the Red Queen, despite all her posturing, her wealth, and her marching army, is completely without a friend. She is completely without love and she is absolutely and unequivocally without any real power. The White Queen, on the other hand, inspires profound loyalty from the people around her with her gentleness. They are ready to die to protect her. The Red Queen inspires nothing but fear and hatred. Her subjects are either praying for her demise or conspiring toward her downfall.

As a man that has walked the fragile precipice between love and hatred, I can attest to the power of gentles, the awe in which the gentle are held, and the power that a person with quiet confidence holds.

The Bible says as much: *The meek shall inherit the earth.* Those with even a little knowledge of the metaphysical realm know that the inheritance is there for the taking—and you don't have to wait until the hear-after. With gentleness as your charge, you can have it all now.

This is another one of those wonderfully, anti-intuitive treasures, hidden in plain sight. You don't spin the planet on its axis by rolling up your sleeves and calling on brute strength. You spin the planet and all that is on it with the simple power of gentleness.

When I was young, I wanted to move heavy weights and kick elephants to death with my Mawashi Geri (roundhouse kick). I thought the soft arts like qui gung, tai chi and mediation were just that, soft. Now that I have been roaming the planet for half a century I realize the naivety of my early evaluations. I was wrong. The power is not in the physical, that is just games played in dojos and dojangs. The real power is in the opposite. That is why my game now has gone to new heights. I have stopped looking for the ostentatious, and instead seek out the aesthetic.

» Warrior Practices:

Gentleness needs to be practiced. The exercises here are all about identifying areas in your life where you are not gentle—with others or yourself. This could include such things as road rage, self harm, family arguments, or work issues. Do any of these relate to you?

I have a friend who treats my kids beautifully. He is gentleness itself with them. Yet at home he is not so kind. He is savagely short-tempered with his own kids, and is abrupt and cutting with his wife and at work. His employees are on eggshells, terrified he might explode in anger at any minute.

Hardly the behavior of a warrior.

How are you with your kids?

How are you at work?

What about in the car. Do you experience road rage?

If you are not balanced in any of these areas, do you find yourself rationalizing? *It's not my fault. It's* (fill in the blank) *the kids, the wife, the workmates, those idiots on the road. They wind me up!*

Your behavior is *your* responsibility. You have to bring it back to you. If you are a self sovereign, then everything that happens in your reality is your responsibility. I refuse to be involved in road rage. It is 10 leagues below my best game. Do you imagine for even a second that someone who is master of their fate and captain of their soul might be seen dead flipping the V's and firing invectives from the driver's seat of his car because someone cut him off? I think not.

And I will not lose my character with those closest to me. I refuse to let that happen, and if it ever did, I would take responsibility immediately and redress.

The self is the self's only friend. The self is the self's only enemy.

Remember the hermetic law *as within as without*. If you are short with your kids it is not them, it is *you*. Their behaviour is just the universe giving you a nudge to let you know you are out of centre.

Examine every area of your life and do an inventory on your behavior. A warrior is not just gentle in the public aspects of his life. He is gentle in all aspects of his life, even when alone.

Being gentle is an inside job. It starts with you. It starts with you being gentle with yourself. Most people talk to and treat themselves worse than their most-hated enemy. You need to be in charge of yourself on every level: what you think , what you say, and what you do. You need to conquer and master the internal dialogue. Don't sit around battering yourself on a daily basis. Your body is touch-sensitive. It listens to you. It hears every communication, and it registers all. If you do not want shit on the hard drive, stop writing shit onto the software.

Of course, we all know that thoughts are firing off in the background all the time, and we seemingly have little sway over them. But thoughts are like everything else in the universe. If you pay them attention, you grow them. If you take the attention away, they fade and die. So feed the thoughts that you want, those that are profiting you, and take attention away from the rest. When they enter your consciousness, don't follow the negative projections. Do not, in your mind's eye, chase the story. If you follow your thoughts as they take you on a myriad of different negative projections, you take yourself out of the present moment and you feed the story. If you feed the story often enough with emotive and constant negative imaging, you will create a self-fulfilling prophecy. You will make your imaginary worst-case scenario into a present reality. Your greatest fears (as the Bible says) will come upon you.

This take practice, but you have the opportunity every minute of every day to do just that.

Write down the areas in your life where you are not gentle, where you think you could improve. Isolate each of these areas and practice the art of *noticing*.

If you have an issue with road rage, I would like you to notice every time you lose your temper in the car. Noticing something that you do habitually will bring light to your behaviour. When you bring light to something you begin its demise. That which is exposed to light must itself become light. Once you *notice*, control the urge to lash out, control the anger. This is where the power is. This is where the warrior spends his time. Anyone can rage in the car, and almost everyone does. It takes great self-control to stop yourself from engaging in this kind of behaviour. Self control is not developed in a vacuum. It is developed by practice.

If you are snappy with the kids, do the same thing. For the next week, notice every time you shout at your children (or the TV, or the radio), and practice holding the rage while finding a more profitable outlet for it.

Remember this. Anger and shouting are violence. It damages as much, sometimes more, than actually physical abuse.

Do you see yourself as a violent father? An abuser of your children? Do you see yourself as a violent husband? If so, stop being violent. Take control. Be gentle, and make gentleness an art form. Master it and see what an amazing difference this very subtle power brings to your health, your wealth, and your relationships.

Chapter Summary:

This chapter is about controlling and respecting your power and never allowing it to spill. Gentleness is the mark of a courageous warrior. He knows that anger and violence are the marks of a raw beginner, so he polishes and finesses his character until he is the personification of the gentle man.

Chapter Four

†

A Warrior is...
Industrious

People complain a lot lately. Have you noticed? They complain about not having enough. They say they don't have enough time, they do not have enough resources, and they feel as though they lack the influences necessary to live a successful life.

Deep down, despite the lamentation, I know and they know, this is a lie. It is simply not true. We all have the same amount of time in our day. Kings, queens, presidents and prime ministers, sportsmen and tycoons all get the same 24 hours as you do. It is what they do with their allotted minutes that sets them apart from everyone else.

We also all have access to the same amount of knowledge. Every book ever written by the greatest men and women of our species is available, free to all, in the libraries of the world. But that knowledge will not fly through the window and land on your lap. You have to go out and get it. As my friend Mark Wood always says, *God feeds the birds, but he does not put the food in their nests for them.*

The onus is on you. If you need influence or guidance or inspiration, do not wait for it to come to you. Instead, make it your definite intention to seek it out.

People have big ideas. I hear them all the time. Big ideas are not unique, they are falling from the trees. Anyone can have big ideas, but it is not enough. On their own, dreams are impotent. It is massive action and dedicated industry that turns the germ of an idea into manifest reality. If you want to turn great information into a great reality you need industry.

If you want your life to be massive, then massive industry is the essential ingredient. This includes industry in your study and industry in your work. The knowledge that you take from books comes to you as raw energy. We call this energy information. To make information valuable, we need to convert it.

Let me give you a for instance.

I read a biography many years ago about Arnold Schwarzenegger, who, in my opinion, is one of the hardest working men on the planet. In the book he talked about his first best seller, which was a fitness book. He recalled how he was told in no uncertain terms that, although the book was good, it fell into a minority genre. Because it had a very niche market, he was warned he should not expect great sales.

Arny is not a man that likes to think or do small. During the Mr. Universe competition some years before, he was facing the colossus that is Lou Ferrigno (the Hulk) in the final showdown. Arny was so confident about his ability, he was so sure he was going to win, he rang his mother before competing in the final and told her that he had already taken the title. When he told Ferrigno this (watch the film *Pumping Iron*), you could literally see the fight running from his veins.

Arny decided, against all the sensible advice and piss-poor odds, that he was going to get to the top of the *New York Times* best-seller list. He took his book and a small team of people and went on the road, visiting cities across the length and breadth of America, promoting his book to everyone that would listen.

True to form, he climbed to the very top of the *New York Times* best-seller list and defied all his critics. Inspiring information I think you'll agree. It lifts you. But on its own, the words remain nothing but simple information, raw energy waiting for conversion. When I read Arny's biography, I had just released a book of my own, *Watch My Back*. I decided to emulate his success and get *my* niche book onto the Sunday *Times* best-seller list as well.

I literally followed his advice step-for-step. I set up a 32-city tour from Portsmouth right up to Edinburgh, Scotland. I promoted my book in every medium, from talks in book shops, to interviews on the radio and appearances on TV. I was profiled in the papers, and a glut of magazines ran interviews with me. *Martial Arts Illustrated* magazine even did a pullout poster listing the details of my tour.

I spent three days in London alone just walking (and Tubing), going from shop to shop, signing stock, talking to customers and staff, and selling books. We sold bucket loads.

Within the first week of publication, we hit the top 20 in the *Times* hardback best-seller list. The next year, I sold three times as many copies in paperback and hit the list again. My wife Sharon and I were pretty much on the road promoting our book for three months at a time. It was a very exciting time and we achieved our goal.

Of course, the impact the tour and the book made attracted a whole new following and readership for my other backlist books. Subsequent books were received with open arms by the industry and the public because I had carved a section for myself in British book shops. It also helped spill my reputation onto the world stage. To date we are in print in 12 different languages and sell copies all around the world.

The success of the book also helped open doors into the world of TV, theatre, and cinema. In fact, *Watch My Back* is now a major feature film (*Clubbed*) that had a cinema release. It was sold to 15 different territories, appeared on TV, and premiered both in London's West End and Paris, France.

I took information and inspiration from a book, and with great industry I converted it into massive action. The results of that action are still sending positive ripples through my life even now, many years after the event.

It is about industry. All the information in the world will not help without massive action. You could have a library of unread books, it won't help. Or perhaps you've read every one of those books back to front, but have not taken any action. It will still not help.

Action is the key.

The warrior knows this and he takes action every day.

You have 24 hours in your day. Make sure that each of those hours is wisely invested.

When I was a full-time martial arts instructor, it was usual for me to physically train three times a day. It was my job. It was what I did. When I wasn't training, I was teaching. When I wasn't teaching, I was studying martial arts. When I wasn't studying, I was writing about it (prolifically). When I wasn't writing, I was conversing with like-minded people. And when I was asleep, I dreamed about the arts. It was my employ, my passion, my life. I made martial arts a magnificent obsession, fully immersing myself into its practice.

What appeared from the outside to be a heavy work schedule was actually just me having a great time. My industry was hardly work at all because I loved every minute of it. I was excited when a new book dropped through the letter box for me to read, and when the monthly MA magazine was delivered. My every day started and ended with martial arts. I take that kind of dedication, that kind of massive industry, into everything I do. I have a finite amount of time in this incarnation, and I intend to do something magnificent with every second of it.

One of the problems I find is that people think they are limited. They believe the universe works in limitation, and they are sure that the fates favour some people more than it favours others. My experience of the world tells me that there are no limitations other than those I set myself. The universe is infinite and will give me as much as I want. In fact the more I draw from it, the more it will proffer. There is abundance and it is all ours. The universe certainly *does* favour some more than it favours others. This is very true. In fact it says as much in the Holy Quran: *God favours those who strive, he favours not those who do not strive.*

The Christian Bible concurs: *Ask and you shall receive, seek and you shall find, knock and the door will open unto you.* Asking and seeking and knocking are actions. To ask, to seek, and to knock is to strive. The more you strive, the more you get. The universe favours those that put themselves forward. What this tells us is that you (and not the universe) decide who the universe favours and who it does not. If you sit on your arse all day and do nothing, nothing much will happen. You will not be favoured, because you are simply not commanding the law. If, however, you get out there and *strive*, then you become favoured. That, my friends, is exciting. It is inspiring. To think that you can court the favour of great forces just by striving for it is an amazing revelation.

Industry is an imperative. You cannot throw out a few press-ups on Monday and expect to look like Adonis for the weekend.

Eddie Izzard, one of the foremost comedians of our day,

is a great example of a man who strives. He is a warrior. He employs massive industry to wring the very best and the very last out of every allotted hour.

As well as being a genre-breaking standup comic, he is also a writer and a Hollywood actor. He even taught himself French so that he could perform his act in Paris in the native tongue.

As you may or may not have heard, he has just (2010) completed 43 consecutive marathons in 50 days, which is more than 1,000 miles of running. How incredible. Forty-three marathons and Eddie is a non-runner. He didn't even train for it—other than doing a two-week prep—which is the same as not preparing.

This is a man who does not believe in limitations. If there is something that he wants to do, he does it. If he doesn't know how to do it, he learns how to do it. If what he wants to do scares the shit out of him, he does it anyway. If time is against him, he manipulates time so that time works for him.

Eddie says that he was massively inspired by the ordinary men and women of the First World War and Second World War. When called to duty, these ordinary folk doing ordinary, every-day jobs, turned into super beings. One minute they were living mundane and simple lives, working in factories and tending to home and children, the next they were flying airplanes, driving tanks, manufacturing munitions, healing the wounded, and saving the world.

They unearthed and discovered and developed high-level skills and great courage in very short periods of time. They did this because demands were placed on them; demands that drew miraculous abilities from within—abilities and skills that they did not even know they had.

Eddie was talking about this on daytime television, and the interviewer quipped dryly, *'all we need is another war then.'*

No, it is not another war we need, it is demand. But demand is most potent when it is placed on us by ourselves. Eddie created the demand to learn French by setting up a gig in France, forcing him to learn the language in a short period of time. He placed the demand on himself to run 43 consecutive marathons by promising publicly to do it for charity. He manufactured demand. He started a small war inside him that said, *fuck I've got to do it now. I am committed.*

Of course, this created discomfort. It was hard, but discomfort is where the warrior collects his power, and 'hard' is what warrior types have for breakfast every day.

We have unfortunately fallen into a period in which people have become soft. They want to make omelets without breaking any eggs. They are looking for growth in comfort. Let me be clear, there is no growth in comfort other than the comfort we find in becoming comfortable with discomfort.

What Mr. Izzard has managed to do by running his 43 marathons is much bigger than raising money for a very worthwhile charity. He has created an 'allowing.' When an unfit man runs 43 consecutive marathons, it automatically allows us all to think bigger. Think better. Think grander. Doing an ordinary marathon, by comparison, suddenly seems very achievable—even mundane.

When *you* strive, when you think and act bigger than ever before, you too will create an allowing, so that others stuck in their small fearful realities will be able to break free with you. Perhaps they will never do standup in a foreign language or run a marathon a day for a whole month, but if it is enough to break them out of a depression, or an illness, or an unfulfilling life, then it will have all be worth the while.

Being industrious and creating big realities also creates an allowing in ourselves. When we achieve what we once thought impossible, it instills in us a belief that anything can be achieved, everything can be accomplished—even impossible things. Eventually, like Lewis Carol's White Queen, we will be thinking six impossible things before breakfast.

» Warrior Practices:

For the warrior practice in this chapter, I would like to encourage you to do another inventory of your week. This one is to account for all your time, so you can see what is available to you and what you are doing with your allotted moments. You might be surprised when you see how much time is lost, how much time is wasted, and how much time is actually spent doing things that do not profit you or anyone else. You may also find that you are spending a lot of time doing things that are better delegated to others.

This inventory will allow you to see where you are wasting time. It will help reveal where you are not using time efficiently, and perhaps where you are not using time at all. If you are in the pub for five hours a night, or spending four hours in front of the TV, that time (or certainly a portion of it), could be used instead to develop and enhance a profitable skill. Even if you only manage to find an extra hour each day, that translates into 365 hours a year that could be used to study and learn something new on a chosen subject.

When I did an inventory of my own week many years ago, I realized that I was spending too much time asleep. I know that sleep is important, but you can have too much of it. There will be plenty of time to sleep when you are dead.

No need to over indulge in it now. Currently we spend a third of our allotted time with our eyes closed. I was getting eight hours a night, but I was pretty sure I could get away with six hours.

People like Condoleezza Rice manage massive workloads on about four hours a night. She gets up at four in the morning to do a training session before her working day starts. If she can do it, I am sure that you and I can too—though we may have to build ourselves up to her level.

I started to get up earlier so I could get more work done, and it made a massive difference. Two hours early in the morning is worth four hours at any other time of the day, because there are absolutely no disturbances. By getting up three hours earlier every day, I found more than 1,000 extra hours a year that I placed directly into profitable activity.

I also noticed from my inventory that I was watching a lot of TV—too much. Sometimes I'd sit in front of the telly all night, spending five hours of watching mostly rubbish. What a waste.

I started to use that time instead to read or study. Five hours is a lot of reading, nearly 2,000 hours worth over 12 months. I got through a library of great books that filled me with powerful information, ready for conversion.

I gave up beer 10 years ago. That means I no longer sit in a pub bar talking bollocks with strangers, or lose hours nightly in a drunken haze. Not only do I save more hours, but my liver gets to breathe another day.

I also found that I was meeting with people—for walks, for talks, and for meetings—that I did not really want to meet. My wife would hear me on the phone agreeing to the meeting, and she'd ask, *Why are you meeting that person? I can tell by your tone that you don't want to.* I was saying 'yes,' because I was afraid to say 'no.'

In the Bible they call this *people-pleasing*, and in the Christian church, people-pleasing is considered a sin. I was wasting so much time meeting people that I didn't want to meet, meeting people for all the wrong reasons, meeting people when my instinct was screaming at me to say *no*.

To counter this, I started to listen to my instinct, that feeling in the pit of the stomach. When it said 'no,' I said 'no.'

I still met with people when it felt right, but when it felt wrong I said, 'no.' I saved myself, not only massive amounts of time, I also saved a lot of energy that would have been wasted otherwise.

There is a time for everything. Our innate instinct will nudge us in the right direction, but only if we listen to it.

If we don't listen, the instinct becomes dulled. When we do heed its direction, it sharpens and hones itself.

I'd also encourage you to look at your working habits. Some people spend a lot of time doing nothing. Like the example I gave earlier, there are people who spend two or three hours at the gym and only do about thirty minutes of work.

Many people waste too much time avoiding the burn in training, in work, in relationships, and in life itself. My council here is the same as it is with building muscle. Get into the burn quickly, and stay in the burn long. If you are at work, do it with full immersion. Nothing else is worth your while.

If you are going to be at work for eight hours, make those eight hours pay. If you find yourself avoiding what you should be doing, hating what you should be doing, or skiving, then maybe you are in the wrong job. Bob Dylan said that a man who could get up in the morning and go to bed at night only having done what he really wanted to do in between, is a success.

Are you doing *only* what you want to do, or is your world filled with undesirable tasks? If it is, then change it. You have that power.

The key I have found is to employ yourself with something that you absolutely love. Work is no longer work, labour is no longer labour, and industry, from morning until evening is an absolute joy. I often find myself waking in the middle of the night to write down ideas for my next article, my new play, or an opus for the cinema. It is a joy. Do you know how easy it is to become good at something you love doing?

In martial arts, people thought my training routine was maniacal. To me, it was just a day's work, a day at the office. If you worked at a computer for eight hours a day would they call you maniacal? No, eight hours would be considered a normal working day—even 10 hours. So why is eight hours on the mat any different? I loved every minute of it.

I write so much that people refer to me as prolific. I would not say that I am prolific, I am just doing something I love all day long. It doesn't take long to fill dozens of books with your ideas when you are at the keyboard eight hours a day. You become good very quickly, and you soon have a library of work behind you. I am just a man doing a job he happens to love. I am doing it out of choice. I made the choice 20 years ago to give up conventional employment and train full time. Later, I gave up training as my employ to write full time. If

I made the choice, then you can make the choice to do what you love.

So look at your working day. Where are you slack? Where can you improve?

I realized looking at my own day that I was very industrious very early in the morning. It was hard to get out of bed at 5 a.m., but once I was up I accomplished an amazing amount of work. By 10 a.m., I'd have almost a full day in. Later in the day, my energy levels were not so strong. I was distracted by other aspects of the business and my output was not so impressive. I started working early in the morning all the time. My output doubled, and I was able to take on more work. I was getting more done, and the quality of my work got better and better.

I have another writer friend who prefers to work through the night. After the midnight hour he comes alive. It is not conventional and it wouldn't suit me, but it works for him. He manages to get a huge amount of work done because he is never disturbed. Who's going to call at three in the morning? No one in their right mind.

Write the inventory. Examine each day. Look at where you can save time, create time, and make time work better for you. Make sure you look at where you are wasting time, then use the wasted time for something better. Discover your own personal secrets of time. When are your most productive hours? What time of the day allows you to turn 120 minutes on the clock into four hours of productivity? I would be very surprised if you can't find at least another five hours in your day to invest in You Inc.

This does not mean, of course, that you should be working around the clock. To be a successful warrior your life has to be balanced. Time with your family is a great investment, as is working alone in the quiet hours of the day. This is merely an exercise to show you where there are leaks in your day, in your week, and in your life.

I would like to encourage you to rediscover the joy of labour, and uncover the forgotten power hidden in your everyday allotment of time.

Chapter Summary

Knowledge without action is impotent. The warrior uses his body as a furnace that moulds information into manifest reality. He finds an employ that is a passion, and he never works again.

Chapter Five

†

A WARRIOR IS...
VIRTUOUS

What is the point of having the whole world if you lose yourself in its acquisition? Virtue is rarely mentioned in these trying times. Even in the halls of supposed power, virtue seems to be lost. It is rare indeed that you meet someone truly virtuous. And yet... and yet that is where our true power lies.

The roman politician Boethius, a wealthy and powerful adviser to Caesar, was perhaps the greatest advocate of virtue, claiming it to be the only real treasure that man needed. According to Boethius, it is the one thing that cannot be taken away by the wheel of fortune.

Boethius was known throughout Rome for his honesty and his integrity, and had built a great fortune. But he was surrounded by many dishonest people who were gravely threatened by his piety. Plotting against him, they had him imprisoned and sentenced to death on trumped up conspiracy charges.

Boethius had all of his worldly goods, titles, and properties taken from him. Left alone in a cell, facing certain death, he wrote a book called *The Consolation of Philosophy* that detailed his thoughts at the time—revelations that can only come from a man facing certain demise.

Troubled initially by his loss of fortune, Boethius was visited in his cell by wisdom in the guise of a beautiful woman. She encouraged him to examine his thoughts and fears, and questioned whether anything of any real value had actually been taken away from him.

After long contemplation, Boethius had an epiphany. He realized that even though he had lost his fiscal wealth, his land, and his family, he still had something that no amount of money could buy. He possessed something that was impervious to the fates, and completely unaffected by the wheel of fortune. He still had his virtues. Nothing could touch them, nor take them away. He realized in this flash of inspiration that he was the most powerful man in the world. And in that moment he found peace. He became fearless, knowing that even death held no sway over him. Even those who had contrived to have him imprisoned would inevitably—at some point—find themselves in a similar position to his. But without the virtue that had been his saving grace, their incarceration would be in hellfire.

A warrior knows the value of virtue, and spends his life cleansing himself from the inside out so that his virtue will be honed. He is committed to truth. He knows that his power is immediately taken if he loses his moral compass.

Recognising that the only lasting treasures are those built from within, the warrior dedicates his life to the development of virtue. He practices honesty, integrity, and morality in everything he does. He does not see things as being small or large. He sees everything—even the minutia—as vital.

The warrior understands that a tiny chip in his moral armoury will quickly be engineered into a gaping hole that will leave him vulnerable. He also understands that his integrity will be tested at every stage of his journey. He pays his taxes down the last penny. He tells the truth even if the truth opens him up to ridicule and criticism. And he develops a profound understanding of himself so he can never escape his own conscience with weak rationalization.

People are generally in denial about their moral health. They kid themselves that they are virtuous and honest men and women with strong integrity, yet they continue to tell lies. Consciously or unconsciously they practice immorality every day. They hide their dishonesty with thinly-veiled self denial, telling themselves that a white lie is not really a lie—though we all know it is.

We see this in the news every day. The politicians that rule the land do not look like warriors, they do not act like warriors, and they do not live like warriors. The newspapers and the news bulletins are filled back-to-front with people building their fortunes at the expense of their integrity.

When people look to their heroes for influence, all they see are celebrities selling their souls to the highest bidder, or famous footballers cheating and fouling on the television. They watch as their MP's and their Ministers, even Prime Ministers, lie publicly, cheat at their expenses, and act immorally in private. You rarely see men and women who are true examples of integrity.

I have lived an immoral life. I have lied, cheated, and stolen. I have been violent, and I have promoted and taught violence. I have sold my integrity for little more that an ego feed, so I know how it feels to live without virtue. When I was in that place I was lost and lonely and sad. I felt weak. I *was* weak. Like Dante on his descent into Satan's lair, I visited all nine circles of the inferno and it literally was hell.

I kidded myself that I was a warrior because I knew how to kill people with my bare hands, using techniques learned in exotic martial arts. But I was no warrior. And I have to tell you, there is no joy in hurting other human beings. When I looked at my broken and scarred face in the bathroom mirror, all I saw looking back at me was a weak man in a fleshy armour. Physically I looked the warrior archetype, but below the muscles, the sinew, and the badges of battle, was a scared boy using violence as a hiding place from true growth.

I have learned that the fight *out there* is much easier than the fight on the inside, the internal jihad that sorts the men from the boys and the pavement scrappers from the true warriors.

What I had done over a decade of mayhem I had to undo. My atonement was long and it was painful, but ultimately it was true. My life became, still is and will continue to be, a warrior's path.

I was not a pseudo warrior, someone that has all the gear but no idea. I went on a proper warrior pilgrimage, where the challenges and the battles and the wars never left the surface of my skin.

The true pilgrimage is one of absolution, where you cleanse every stain until all that is left is one virtuous lump of you. This has been my journey thus far, and it continues to be my journey, ever onward.

We all need to understand ourselves and develop the tools that will enable us to mercilessly flush out and dissolve character flaws, negative sub-personalities, and shadows that hide inside. This takes real courage. There is nothing more frightening than coming face to face with your own shadows.

» Warrior Practices:

The virtues are our most precious commodities. People with real power spend every day honing them. So I encourage you here to make a list of all the virtues. Work on strengthening the ones that are weak, and polishing and maintaining the ones that are already strong.

These are the virtues as written down by one of the most successful and respected leaders in the history of our species: Benjamin Franklin.

Temperance: Eat not to dullness. Drink not to elevation.

The first power of temperance is in knowing what temperance is. As I said earlier, people hide from their shadows and weaknesses because they are afraid of them. They kid themselves that they are eating and drinking in moderation, when really they are consuming to excess. They are in denial. They see an alcoholic as someone who sits on a park bench having it large from a brown paper bag. They do not understand that many alcoholics only drink over the weekend, but they do it to excess. Some only consume in the evening, but they cannot go a single night without a drink. Denial is the devil. It kids you into thinking you are moderate and that you do not have a problem, when really you are a raving addict.

My friend had a heart attack recently, and it shook him to his very foundation. At just 50, he never expected to be having an attack of the heart so young. After having a by-pass operation he went straight to the pub, consumed a lot of beer and filled himself to the chest with a very heavy three-course meal.

As he was consuming, he and his wife sat and talked about how puzzling it was that he'd had a heart attack when he eats so healthily and drinks so moderately. In truth, he has been drinking and eating too much for too many years. Everyone knows it—except him... and his wife.

She can't admit his excess. How can she? She's in on the denial. To admit that he has a problem is to admit that she has a problem, and that is a truth that neither of them wants to consider.

I had another friend, deceased now, who drank too much. I told him so. I loved him, so I felt I had to be truthful. He didn't believe me, told me I was wrong. His wife of 50 years told him the truth too, more times than I care to remember. But of course, she was wrong as well. What did she know? She was just trying to take his beer off him, he said, and that was not about to happen. He'd worked all his life for a beer. He'd earned it.

Eventually the doctor told him the truth too. He *was* drinking to excess. But my friend said, *What the fuck do doctors know? The doctor is wrong.*

My friend died of his disease, still in denial.

I have lost two family members so far to denial, and I have lost more friends than I care to count. Consumption is not the problem. Denial is the problem. Being a warrior is about brutal self honesty. It is about knowing yourself inside and out so that you cannot get away with kidding yourself. As far as a warrior is concerned, denial is death. It is way below his game.

Know what is good for you and what is bad. Make it your business to know.

Be aware of where your limits are and do not allow yourself to cross them. If you do cross them, admit that you crossed them, even if only to yourself. Then train yourself not to cross them again.

Know that everything outside of homeostasis (natural balance) is pornography. Excess is porn. Do not be a dealer in porn. It is below your game.

As I said in Chapter Two, a warrior seeks self mastery, and the first rule of mastering the self is mastering the palate.

Silence: Speak not but what may benefit others or yourself. Avoid trifling conversation.

Silence is power. All the sages have said as much, and the bibles concur. Even the prophets agree: Jesus, Mohammed, Krishna, Buddha, Lau Tzu, Guru Granthe Sahib. The philosophers too: Hermes, Socrates, Plato, Aristotle, Gurdjieffe, Dante, Milton, Blake. They all say the same thing, that God, the Universe, the Divine Mind, the Collective Unconscious, the Higher Power, He, It, She, They, all communicate with us through silence. The big truths are hidden in plain sight.

We are sitting right on top of all the knowledge in the universe, and we do not see it because it is hidden right in front of our face. Like a fly sitting on a TV screen we are lamenting, *What picture? I can't see any picture.*

When we practice silence, we allow natural intuitions to

converse with us. We can ask questions and receive answers. We can access the unknown. We can merge with God. It takes faith to find silence of course, and courage, because so many people are looking for the answers in noisy places. When you tell someone to look in the quiet, they think it is a fool's errand.

But I implore you to listen to your gurus, read your bibles, heed your philosophers, and more than anything, try it for yourself so you can be your own prophet. Be quiet in your thinking, quiet in your communications, and quiet in your life.

The traditional way of finding quiet is through meditation. Many people see meditation as a waste of time. They can see no power here. I have had neophytes get angry with me when I recommend meditation as a way of garnering power. They want to move things around manually. They want to break their backs digging for power, but they see power as being an association of brute force. There is no real power there. The power is in silence.

Others complain that they can't sit still long enough to meditate. It is not in their nature. I disagree. It is our inherent nature to find quiet, sit in quiet, and grow in this magnificent fertilizer. It is just that many of us have lost contact with our nature. We live in a busy, noisy world where there are very few opportunities to access quiet. We have to make the effort to find time and space, and access it ourselves.

The best times to meditate are very early in the morning before the rest of the world awakens, and the last thing at night when everyone else closes down. Consistency is the key with meditation. *Now and again* will not garner any great result. Twice a day, every day, is good. Twenty minutes at a time is enough in the beginning. You can increase this as you become more proficient. Once you are practiced, you will be able to find quiet anywhere, and you will be able to experience quiet everywhere, even in the very busy and loud places.

Here is the method I practice, bearing in mind that there are many methods of meditation. Find a quiet room. Switch off the phones. Ask your family not to disturb you under any circumstance. If you feel that there is even the slightest chance of being disturbed, you will not achieve a deep level of mediation. Sit cross-legged on a cushion. Close your eyes or keep them open if you prefer. I close mine. Locate your breath. Keep your attention on your breath. Follow it in and follow it out. Your attention will try to drift away from it and follow thoughts that flood into your mind. Parts of you will resist the meditation process, because parts of you will be dissolved by the quiet. This is because God is in the quiet. This is because those parts of you that are dissolved by the quiet are the parts of you that need to be dissolved, or at least, brought under your control.

Override the resistance that may arise. Of course it will be difficult—if it were easy there would be no benefits and everyone would be doing it. You have to work hard for your power. Do not expect it without work. All you get without work is laziness, which comes by the barrow load.

Follow your breath in and out. The attention that you are placing on your breath needs to be developed. Like a muscle, you need to build its strength. If you find it hard at first to hold the attention, don't worry. Your attention will get stronger every time you exercise it. Stay on the breath. Feel as though you are inside the breath. Imagine that you are on top of the breath like a vehicle, and it is carrying you into higher places. Eventually, you will feel as though you are the breath.

By holding your attention on the breath, ignoring any thoughts that try to enter you mind, you will eventually find quiet. Once you are there, sit in the quiet. Rest there. Stay there as long as you are able. It will be subtle at first, but when you practice regularly, you will start to feel differently.

You will become calmer and naturally more quiet. You will start to have strong intuitions about things. Great ideas will just pop into your head, and your understanding of things will become enhanced. When obstacles or difficulties arise in your life, meditation will be like an oracle that you can visit in your search for answers.

As I said, consistency is the key. You need to add fold over fold and layer over layer to your practice.

Order: Let all your things have their places. Let each part of your business have its time.

There is a time for work and there is a time for play. There is a time for being serious and there is a time to laugh. Many people mix these things up and end up multi-tasking. They work while they are with their children, and play when they are at their work. Some people become too serious all the time; others think that everything is a laugh. It takes wisdom to know when to push and when to yield. It takes great strength to stop yourself from pushing when you should be yielding, and yielding when really the situation demands a big push.

I see friends of mine, who think of themselves as powerful men and women, spend their time at the beach on holiday with their lap-tops or their blackberries. If not taking calls from work, they are anticipating calls from work. If they are not working on their lap-tops, they are certainly contemplating work.

Let me be clear. If you are working, work. If you are at play, be at play. Whatever you are doing, immerse yourself into it fully or don't do it at all. Be powerful enough to stay present with the doing. Otherwise you are never really anywhere, and your lack of focus will attract and grow weakness.

When I am on holiday, the phone is off. I inform my friends and customers that I am on holiday and out of contact. They understand. If I am with my kids, I am not taking calls about business and doing deals that *can't wait*. There is no power here.

Similarly, when I am resting, I am resting. When I am with my wife, I am only with my wife. Everything needs its place. You need to work very hard and be in the burn to grow. But you need to rest hard and play hard too. When you are with your kids you are dad—not a big business man. You are not a philosopher, you are just a dad (or a mum). So be that. Be present. See what an amazing difference this makes to the quality of their lives. See what a difference it makes to the quality of your life.

You may kid yourself that the kids *hardly know* you are

working when you are with them, but that would be naïve. It's as bad as saying *they hardly know I smoke around them.* They know. It is in the air. It is on your clothes, and leaking out of your pores. Be present. Immerse yourself in the moment.

This takes practice. When you practice diligently you get good. It's as simple as that. So practice.

Resolution: Resolve to perform what you ought. Perform without fail what you resolve.

It is imperative that you get a series of successes behind you if you want to live a successful life. Success becomes your blueprint for all future goals. If you get a series of failures behind you or a series of tasks uncompleted, then each new task is going to be that much harder to achieve. How can it be otherwise when all your reference points are negative?

Your successes and completions do not need to be huge. Even small successes, little tasks completed, will build your confidence to the point that you will see anything as achievable.

Getting my fist book into print took me a long time. I was in my early 30s before I secured a spot on the shelves at Waterstones. The main reason for this was not that my work was unprofessional, it was because I did not completely believe I could make my dream a reality. When I was finally able to get the book into print, the flood gates opened. I wrote five books in the next year, and have since published 35.

The belief of getting one book into print set up a positive blueprint. I followed that and was able to replicate my first success again and again. It also tripled my confidence. If I can publish one book, why not two books? Why not three? What is there to stop me from making a living as a writer of books?

Furthermore, if I can publish a book, why not a stage play? And if I can get a play on, why not a film? If I can successfully make a film, what is there to stop me from winning a BAFTA or an Oscar?

You can see how completion begets more completion, and success begets more success. This is one of the reasons why a warrior will not start something that he does not intend to complete. He thinks long and hard before committing himself to a project, because he knows that failure to complete can have a devastating effect on future successes. Make certain that if you start something, you finish it.

Frugality: Make no expense but to do good to others or yourself. Waste nothing.

A warrior knows he must respect energy in all its forms. Money is one of the shapes that we make with our energy. If we are capable, we make big shapes with it, acting as caretakers to insure that the flow of wealth continues unhindered. We invest what we have wisely, and we keep money working and multiplying for us.

But lucre, like all other forms of energy, must be respected. It should neither be wasted nor squandered. The rich are rich because they understand the power of their riches. Wealth can be very hard to create, but ludicrously easy to fritter away. We see examples of this every day in the news. The old saying that "a fool and his money are soon parted," could not be more accurate.

If you have become adept at making the money, respect your manifestation at all times. If you don't, what you worked so hard for will stop working hard for you, ending up as numbers on someone else's statement sheet.

Making the money shape is an art form in itself, and making it work for us takes skill and practice. People crave money, even though they have no idea how to use it. Everyone knows that money can buy material things, but few realize that, misused and misunderstood, it can also cause untold misery.

If you are interested in money—what it is, what it represents, and how to make it work for you, then I recommend that you make money the focus of your study.

We can only really control what we understand. There are a million good guides out there that can teach you if you make it your job to learn.

Industry: Lose no time. Be always employed in something useful. Cut off all unnecessary actions.

I talked about this extensively in Chapter 4, so please refer back for detail.

Sincerity: Use no hurtful deceit. Think innocently and justly. And if you speak, speak accordingly.

This is all about becoming an individual. Hurtful deceit is a bad habit for many people that often manifests itself on the social pages of the World Wide Web. Millions allow themselves to be possessed by this habit, deliberately lambasting people in an anonymous forum. It is easy to do. Any fool can do it, and the world is full of fools. Do not be one of them. It is not a warrior trait to be insincere. It is not a warrior habit to think and speak other than honestly and innocently. The philosopher William Blake said, "when you speak the truth, you always avoid a base man." One of the lovely by-products of having sincerity and speaking the truth is that base people will avoid you, and those that want to live in denial will give you a very wide berth.

Being an individual means separating yourself from

the tabloid nation, and staying away from those that cheat, lie, and hurtfully attack others. It is hard. Of course it is. It means changing the habits of a lifetime. It might even mean offending some of your friends who will not like the new you, the upbeat, positive thinker. It shall definitely mean losing parts of yourself, like the part that likes to gossip. That part of you no longer serve your new regime.

If you want to see this in action, go onto one of the many martial arts forums on the Internet and observe. You will see the *pseudonyms* on the message board and how the Mushashis dishonour themselves. As you observe their behaviour towards each other, vow to never emulate it. Promise yourself that their weak, base, and inhuman treatment of one another will always be nine circles below your game.

Remember, this negativity may start innocently enough. But gossip is insidious, and very quickly becomes vile if you allow it any oxygen.

My middle daughter, Lisa, is very adept at avoiding gossip and avoiding gossipy people. She counters negativity with a positive comment, or she does not get involved in the conversation at all. In this aspect of her life, she is a true warrior. The effect of this is wonderful. People in her company are always on their best game, because she forces them to her level. Many people cannot even exist at her altitude. The air is too thin for them and they cannot breathe.

One day, when she was with her boss and two fellow workers driving to an engagement, the group began to gossip about one of the men with whom they all worked. The boss gossiped, and the other two girls joined in. Being the only one that did not speak, it became quickly clear to everyone in the car that Lisa was not taking any involvement in the personal dismantlement of her fellow worker.

The boss became aware of this and directly asked Lisa what she thought of the man in question. Lisa simply told the truth. She liked him, and thought he was a nice, gentle man. The air was thick with silence for a second, and then the boss spent the next half-hour trying to justify her feelings towards the man. Lisa did not answer, other than to underline her opinion of him.

After that one journey, the boss never gossiped with Lisa again. She probably even disliked her, embarrassed by Lisa's forthrightness and rare individuality. Lisa was not worried about that at all. She knows that life is not a popularity contest. Being a warrior means being sincere. You will find that some people are offended by someone rich in sincerity, because it highlights just how poor they are.

This is another virtue that needs to be practiced. With society being as it is, there will never be a shortage of people or situations to practice this virtue on.

Justice: Wrong none by doing injuries or omitting the benefits that are your duty.

Justice takes courage by the bucket, and the courage it takes can only be developed in the arena. You cannot expect to develop courage outside of fear. It will not be grown separately in a culture dish. A warrior knows this, so courts *conscious labour and deliberate suffering.*

In other words, he courts the situations that most people avoid. He grows his courage through fear, and shops for power through suffering. He does not need to wait in a queue, there are no queues on the battlefield. Go into any gym and you will not find anyone queuing up for the squat rack. The warriors are the only ones rushing to the squat rack. One of the cheapest fighting systems to train in is Judo, and yet there are no queues at the dojo door. That is how you know it is good.

Why are there no queues? Because it is such a demanding discipline, probably the best-kept secret in the martial arts. Courage is not the lack of fear. It is acting despite the fact you are scared. When you are scared and do the thing that scares you, courage grows—as sure as a flower grows towards the light.

The warrior develops skills and knowledge that would easily enable him to hurt and take advantage of others less informed. This is why they say, with knowledge comes responsibility. The more skills you develop and the more information you get, the easier it becomes to misuse it.

I was recently asked to write a treatment for a powerful television company, but they didn't want to pay me. I asked why a company worth millions did not want to pay for a simple treatment. They said they didn't want to pay because they didn't have to pay. With the recession on, money was tight. Writers were so desperate for work, they were willing to forgo their pay just to get a foot in the door.

This company showed me how little integrity they possessed when they arrogantly announced they were going to take advantage of people's fear and get them to work for nothing. Needless to say, I didn't work for them. The very fact that they didn't have to pay was an opportunity for them to say, *we don't have to pay and that is precisely why we are paying.* That would have been a rare and magnanimous display of integrity.

People that have power and take advantage of their power for their own short-term profit are not warriors. Eventually they will lose the favour of the powers. Eventually they will lose their money, and worse than that, they will lose their virtue. And virtue is worth more than Solomon's fortune.

Moderation: Avoid extremes.

The monk Bodhidharma created what is known in Buddhism as the middle way. He felt that anything outside of the middle way was pornographic, so he taught the avoidance of excess in all its forms. As a younger man, I experienced many extremes with training, with sex, with my consumptions, and with my opinions. I practiced austere abstinence with food and drink, I trained until I fell over with exhaustion, and I read until I was nearly blind. What I learned from my excess was that any extreme takes you away from your essence.

Blake said that the road of excess leads to the palace of wisdom. I found this to be deadly accurate. The wisdom I found on that road taught me that it is not wise to keep going to extreme places. If you do, one of these days you might not come back. It is a real possibility. Many people live extreme lives, and on the surface, they look as though they escaping the consequence. Then one day, out of the blue, everything they invested into their extremities catches up with them and it is too late.

I have a friend who had been indulging in excess for many years. He'd had a few warnings with health issues and money problems, but he has always ignored them, believing himself somehow impervious to karmic law. Then one day, out of the blue yonder, he decided to stop his excess. He came off the drugs, stopped the alcohol, killed the cigarettes, and started to eat healthy. But he had accelerated so hard with his historical excess that slamming on the brakes did not stop the momentum off his past actions. It all caught him up and he hit the wall with a fatal bang.

Before the age of religion, the Druids worshipped the power of nature and their god was called the Wyrd (as in weird). They did not have a word in their vocabulary for the future, the present or the past. All they had was: *things doing, things done,* and *things owed*.

Things doing was what we'd call the present moment, the things we do in the here and now. *Things done* referred to the past. The things we do today, filter back into the past and become part of god or the Wyrd. *Things owed,* referred to the future. What we do today filters immediately into our past, it joins with the Wyrd, and in time will be given back to us in the future. So according to their belief, our future consists only of what we are owed. And what we are owed, good bad, or indifferent, comes from what we do every day.

To sum it up, if you want to experience a fantastic future, all you have to do is invest fantastically in the future by being very busy and very positive in the *now*. Equally, those who are excessive or negative in the present moment, will by their actions be sowing the seeds for their own future downfall.

If you do not want an excessively bad future, do not create one for yourself by dealing in excess today.

In spirituality we would know this as karma. In science it is called cause and effect. All the bibles tell us that God knows what everyone does. He keeps a perfect record with no omissions. In other words, everything that is thought, said, and done becomes a part of the Wyrd and you will be guaranteed to see it again.

When you understand and work with the law, it allows you to have a hand in your own future. On the other hand, if you are ignorant of the law, don't understand the law, or understand the law but flout it anyway, your future is in your hands, but may not be a bright one.

This is a basic law that the warrior masters and works so that it is profitable.

Ignore the Wyrd at your own peril.

Cleanliness: Tolerate no uncleanness in body, clothes or habitation.

I once had a student who wanted to be a master. When I told him he had bad body odor from poor grooming, he was affronted. He said that I should judge him by what was on the inside, not what was on the outside. I tried to explain that what I was seeing, smelling, and in some cases, tasting, *was* what was on the inside—and it was leaking out everywhere.

As within as without, the ancient Hermetic law states so succinctly.

My student didn't get it then, and he still doesn't get it now. That is why he has slipped into an excessive life. That is why he is not a warrior. Personal hygiene in your body, your clothes, and your home are vital. It is very easy to see the state of a man's mind simply by looking at the state of his keeping. I have yet to meet a powerful man or woman that was not in charge of all aspects of their lives, starting with their bodies and working outwards to the world of men.

When I worked as a bricklayer, we had a rule that served as the cornerstone of our trade. Whether you were building a wall, a house, or a factory unit, the first course of bricks or blocks was the most important. If the first course was out of line by even a millimeter, it'd be out by a yard by the time you reached the roof. That first line of bricks determined that stability of the whole building. For that reason, the best bricklayer on site was always commissioned to lay out the first course of every building, with the other bricklayers following and building upwards from his line.

Personal grooming is the first course of bricks. It is pivotal in the foundation of a warrior's life. If he is out by a small amount on this first course, by the time he reaches the roof he too will be so off course he might never get back to balance again. If he does not even have the personal discipline to look after *the one thing* (himself), how the hell is he going to cope with *the ten thousand things*. (Lau Tzu called the physical world *the ten thousand things*).

The warrior's philosophy is that the real battles are local. It is harder to master the simple things like palate and grooming than it is to climb an icy mountain. If you can master the microcosm then the macrocosm will look after itself.

Look at any army and you will see that personal grooming is paramount in the training of a soldier. They are taught to be meticulous in every aspect of their lives. If they are remiss with the small things, you can be sure they will be completely out-of-control with the big things. In warfare, as in life, that can prove costly—it could even prove fatal.

As I said earlier in my analogy about the night club door, if you let in one gangster you open the door to all gangsters. The same rule applies with personal habits. Let in one addiction, and you open the door to all addictions.

The law works its magic on all things. If your personal grooming is weak, that fragile link will eventually compromise the whole chain.

Tranquility: Be not disturbed at trifles, or at accidents common or unavoidable.

A warrior does not get caught up in trifles. It is definitely and unequivocally below his game. The moment I see people getting upset over petty disputes, minor incidents, or silly arguments, I think to myself, 'beginner,' 'amateur,' 'neophyte.'

People tell me that they are a master of this, an expert in that, or a professor of the other, and then I see them squabbling over opinions on the forums, getting involved in road rage incidents, or starting an argument over a minor incident. This tells me they are no more a master of themselves than they are a Martian on a visit from outer space.

You can tell a warrior by the way he conducts himself in all his dealings. The small incidents just discussed are leagues below a warrior. In fact, these small occurrences would not be able to exist in his orbit for even a few seconds before being burned out by the stratosphere.

As the poet Virgil said to a flagging Dante Alighieri as he struggled through nine circles of the inferno, *there are steeper climbs ahead.* If you are going to get caught out by the minutia, what chance will you have when the bigger challenges present themselves, as they are bound to do?

Chastity: Rarely use venery but for health and for offspring: never to dullness, weakness, or the injury of your own or another's peace or reputation.

Any excess is an excess too far.

Sex is natural between two loving people. It can be healthy, even tantric; it connects you to God. So if sex is good for you, does that mean that more sex is better? Not really. Food is good for you, but too much of the stuff will kill you. Water is vital for life, but drink in one pint too many and water will kill you as sure as cyanide. Exercise is fabulous, but over train and bits will start falling off you.

Too much sex is the same as too much anything. It is addictive. It is seductive. And if you do not master its energy it will run away with all your power.

The lure towards excess is all around us. As little as a five-mile trip to work in the car can expose you to hundreds, even thousands, of pornographic images, tempting you to indulge in excess food, drink, sex, cars, holidays. The messages are plastered all over the news, emblazoned across advertising posters, displayed in shop windows, and pasted onto billboards. You are being teased, tempted, perhaps even brainwashed, just about every minute of every day into believing that pornography is good. It might not advertise itself as porn, but anything outside of natural balance is excess. Once you recognize that the advertisers are out to get you (your money, anyway), it is much easier to tighten your conscious filter and block it all out.

Too much sex is not good for you, just the same as too much anything is not good for you. Because sex feels so nice, too much sex can be very alluring. Moderation is the key. To be a warrior, you need to be a master of all your faculties. Not least sex.

Humility: Imitate Jesus and Socrates.

Humility is a powerful asset. It is not something you can act. If you act it, you are being falsely modest, and there is no power in that. It lacks congruence, and without congruence, we become a vessel of empty noise. True modesty does not need to speak. It is evident the moment you walk into a room.

Modesty does not mean that you need to lie. You don't need to call yourself *Master Wong's worst student* when you know damn well that it is not true. If you are Master Wong's best student, there is no sin in saying so. Honesty is the key.

I was at a friend's wedding some years ago, when he pointed out a friend of his in the corner of the room. He informed me that his friend was the top skydiver in the country. Later, when I got talking to the man in question I said, *I hear that you are the top skydiver in the country.* He simply and modestly said, *yes I am.* He told me there were a lot of better players than him in Europe, and that he still felt he had a lot to learn, but in this country he was the top of the pile. I loved it. I loved him. I loved his confidence. I loved the fact that he didn't have to feign modesty.

If you are good at something, it is liberating to acknowledge that to yourself and to others. I see many people that do not reach their full potential because they have played their skills down so many times with self modesty that they eventually believe it themselves.

As a man with a great faith in God, I know—and I am happy to tell people—that I cannot do anything without

God. It all comes from Him.

But I am also aware that God needs me to be a warrior if I am going to be a powerful conduit for Him. I am also aware that my best stuff is God working through me. I can feel it. He picks up all my flavours on his way through—but ultimately it is all Him.

I am also aware that to be God's tool I need to be courageous, acknowledge my part in the equation, and not play it down. I have found that if I feel the need to tell everyone about my achievements, my qualifications, and my power, it is probably not my true self talking. It is more likely to be a juicy ego looking for a pat on the back or a praise-snack. I always look out for this, and practice restraint when the urge comes through to say *I won a so-and-so award for my last film.* I find that when you don't mention your achievements and people later find out—as they always do—the effect is much more powerful.

If you are not naturally modest, practice restraint until you are. It is a great warrior trait. And if your presence alone does not tell people who you are, then you need to finesse your character more. What you are, who you are, and what you have achieved should be evident without announcement. Your presence should be like an unspoken power that follows you into the room. People should be able to look at you and *know*, even though they might not immediately understand what it is that they know.

I have a very good example of this that occurred when I was teaching my masterclass in Coventry on *self defense against the self*. During the morning session, I was explaining how our aura is expanded through *the power of experience*. Following the afternoon break, the students were listening to some lecture material on the power of shedding and sharing secrets, when a visitor walked into the room dragging an acre of powerful aura behind him.

It was an old friend who had come to visit, John 'Awesome' Anderson, a mentor from my bouncer days. Every head in the room turned to look as John entered. A few mouths opened, and one or two of the students whispered to each other, impressed, 'who the fuck is that?'

John is an impressive man, a physically powerful weightlifter with 20 years of door experience under his belt. He has dealt with violence and violent people in the worst situations, and now teaches the martial way. He is the epitome of a warrior. When I saw John, I was just as surprised as everyone else because his visit was unannounced.

I introduced him to my students as my mentor, and the

room broke into a spontaneous applause. No one had to tell these people to be impressed. Indeed, most admitted afterward they did not know who John was by name or reputation. However, when he walked into the room *they knew who he was*. He spoke with people. He was quiet and humble, and he served as a perfect example to my earlier lecture.

If you want to read more about John, he is featured throughout my biographical tales in *Watch My Back*.

The virtues are your only real treasure. You need to invest in them every day. When you have them, it will be evident to everyone—they will not need to be announced. Virtues are like a human loadstone that will attract everything you need. Invest in them. It will bring a greater return than any stocks or bonds.

Start now. Today. No excuses. Warriors do not deal in excuses.

Chapter Summary:

The real treasures are buried inside us and whilst the warrior may work with the treasures of the external world, he will never mistake them for the kingdom of God, which is within.

Chapter Six

†

A Warrior...
Makes No Excuses

We live in an age of excuses. Everyone has a reason why they failed, a finger poised and ready to point towards the cause of their failure.

When people make excuses they tell you a lot about themselves. They give you a schematic of their inner self. Warriors they are not.

The warrior takes ownership of his universe and everything in it.

Before you can change the world, you have to accept responsibility for your own orbit and develop sovereignty over all you are. A warrior is his own Alpha. He is his own Omega.

Most people consciously, or unconsciously, make excuses when their lives are not going to plan. They give away all their power to blame. Their bad health, their unhappiness, their unemployment, their failing relationships, and their entire sorry life is never their fault. It is always the error of someone else. They never look to themselves for blame or fault, and because of this, they become disempowered.

The warrior makes no such excuses. Like the Zen archer that misses his target, he always comes back to himself for the sauce of error.

I know this is true is because I spent the first three decades of my life blaming others for my sorry lot. During that time, I discovered that once you start blaming, there is no end to it. It is the most debilitating thing a human being can do. The very act of blaming someone else automatically places your power in their hands. If you blame your mum, she has your power. It means that you have to wait for her to act favourably before your problem can be solved. If you blame your schooling, then your teachers have your power. If you blame the environment, your city, your country, your government, the terrorists, the communists, the fundamentals or God, then you give over all your power to the object of your blame. You become powerless.

People give away their power way too easily, because they fear taking responsibility for their own incarnation. They are scared. Yes, blamers are scaredy-cats. It is easy to blame. That is why so many people do it.

Actually, we are taught to blame. The newspapers teach us, the TV teaches us, the schools teach us. There is big business in blame. We are constantly being offered large amounts of money to blame others. You can sue someone (*no win-no fee*) because you fell off a ladder and broke your wrist. You can claim thousands of pounds, because nothing is your fault. If you burn your mouth on a coffee from McDonald's' because *it was too hot,* you can sue because it was someone else's fault. There are solicitors out there right now begging for your business, because litigation means money.

But you know and I know, there is absolutely no power in blame. No matter how attractive it might appear, it is the most debilitating thing you can do. By blaming others, you give away your power. By blaming anything outside of yourself, you disconnect with your own essence.

Blame is not the trait of a warrior. That is why he is so powerful. He sees every hurdle and pitfall in his life as *his* opportunity to develop new skills and enhance/sharpen old skills. He knows that difficulty is where the power lies, and there is nothing so difficult as taking responsibility for your own life. So he never blames.

I have a very good friend who has just experienced a tragedy in his life. His son was stabbed in the heart by a troubled friend he was trying to help. My friend is a stoic from the warrior cast, and his son, who was stabbed several times, is of the same ilk. All of the doctors agreed that he was unlikely to survive. Everyone could have legitimately allowed all their attention to fall upon the attacker. 'Why wasn't he locked up years ago?' They could have fallen into the trap of futility. 'Why has this happened? The universe is so unkind.' In fact, they could have found a glut of ready people outside of themselves and their situation to blame.

But this is a family of warriors. They spend their life teaching the martial way, and showing people how to live a brave life. They know that this is not in their teaching, and more importantly, they know that blaming, even looking for blame or flirting with blame, would not change the situation one bit. So instead, they turned all their attention to their son, and put all their energy into helping him heal.

On one particularly painful day, when the doctors had to insert pipes into the lad's lungs to drain the fluids collecting there, his dad reminded him that very few people ever walk the path that he was now walking. He was on a deathly precipice, the way was treacherous and it was challenging in the extreme. My friend advised him with great love and compassion to embrace the challenge and reap as much power as he could from it. He was where he was. Of course, no one wanted him to be there, but that fact could not be changed. What *could* be altered was his perception to the situation. He could see this path as unique, and his pain as having a strong purpose. In that way, he could honour that pain. He could throw a pail into his reservoir of suffering and draw from it.

When Victor Frankle, a Holocaust survivor during the Second World War, wrote the seminal book about his experiences, *Man's Search For Meaning*, he said he could not change the fact that he was in a concentration camp; he could not alter the fact that people were dying all around him every day; or that he was separated from his wife and in physical and emotional agony. However, he could choose the way he reacted to the dire circumstance. He could decide (and he did decide) to honour his pain. By choosing to meet the challenge that life had given him, he transformed his situation. He became in concert with the universe. Delving into his pain instead of recoiling away in horror, he was able to conspire with universal powers to create the miraculous, out of what was the most heinous experience. Victor Frankle's story has been little less that transformational to millions of people around the world.

At the entry level, the warrior uses everything in his life, good and bad, as grist. So if something happens to him that does not have its genesis in him—in other words, if he cannot see why or how he was at fault—he still resists the urge to look for blame. Rather, he gets on with the job of redressing the balance.

At the level of mastery, when the warrior has a profound understanding of his universe, he recognises that, metaphysically, there are no accidents, The genesis of everything in his orbit starts with him. Knowing this, he is empowered. He knows that if the problem is in him, then the solution is also in him. That is very exciting—and perhaps a little scary —because it means taking responsibility for your world.

Ultimately it is exhilarating, because knowing that it starts and ends with you, gives you the opportunity to get to work creating the fantastic life you've always wanted.

Let me offer you a small example. Recently, someone ran into the back of my car when I was parked legally on the side of the road outside my mother-in-law's house. I wasn't even in the car at the time. I was inside the house having a cup of tea. When I heard the loud bang outside, I knew that someone had crashed into my Jag.

Sure enough, when I went outside I found a car, driven by a very distressed young girl, buried into my back bumper. I took her inside the house and calmed her down while my mother-in-law made everyone a cup of tea. When she was calmer, I exchanged insurance details.

Externally, the fault was hers. That much was clear to everyone. She had been day-dreaming (or texting, or using her phone), and simply did not see my car.

Internally though, I knew that at some level I had created the crash. I went through my usual *internal inventory* and realised that I was out of balance. Specifically, I was out of balance with my car. After much deliberation, I realised that my expensive sports car had drawn a vanity shadow out of me that needed to be dissolved.

There was nothing wrong with this beautiful Jaguar XKR. In fact, it was like a piece of sculpture with a large roaring engine. And there is nothing wrong with owning a car like this. I think everyone should own one. (You can see God better from an XKR). But being brutally honest with myself, I could see that I was not driving the car for the experience of driving the car, I was driving it—in fact I owned it—because a small part of me felt insignificant and under confident. Buying an expensive motor and driving it through the streets of my home city fed that part of me.

When I failed to recognise this, the universe gave me a few little nudges. Three to be exact. I had three minor, but expensive, crashes. I later referred to these as my 'vanity crashes,' which made the problem very clear to me. What had drawn me to the car in the first place was an ego shadow, one that needed to be dissolved or brought to order. It was not in keeping with my warrior quest. The moment I understood this, I let the car go, and the shadow dissolved. It was not easy. The 'Jag' part of me did not want to surrender its prize. It desperately wanted to hold onto the vehicle. In fact, it felt ashamed to let it go, as though without the car it was not complete, and everyone would see that.

I use this kind of understanding in every aspect of my life. I realise that I am part of a frighteningly powerful species. Simply by being out of balance, we can attract all the wrong elements into our life. Once you understand this, you are inspired to seek balance. You will realize that balance is like a magnet, a load stone that will draw abundance into your life.

A warrior strives for balance in everything he does. He never makes excuses.

» Warrior Practices:

Identification is the key, so I invite you to identify all the areas in your life where you are apportioning blame to others. You need to be brutally honest. If there is a part of you that wants to fight for your right to be angry at people, if there is some small or large element that insists on holding onto your blame, especially if it feels righteous or indignant, put it down on a piece of paper and examine it.

Ask yourself one thing. Is this anger, this vitriol, this righteous indignation making me more powerful, or is it just keeping me in a weak and dark place?

If you were abused 20 years ago and that has affected your life in a bad way, you are bound to be angry. I had years of righteous anger about being sexually abused as a boy, and for three decades I lashed out and attacked anyone that even remotely threatened my right to that indignation.

I blamed my abuser for the depression I suffered. I blamed him for my insecurity, and I blamed him for the unsuccessful life that I was living. But using blame did not take away my pain. It did not take away my problems, and it did not make me successful. What it did do was keep me locked in the place of abuse.

Someone that had abused me as an 11-year-old boy was still abusing me when I was 40 years old. When I was 11, I had no choice. I was where I was and felt powerless at that vulnerable age to do anything about it. But at 40, I did have a choice. I was a man, not a baby. I could stop the abuse whenever I wanted to. Even though the abuse was no longer actual, it was still very real to me. As a man, I had the power to change this, but I wasn't using it. I wasn't using it because the anger and the indignation were too delicious to release. I revelled in my anger. It was mine. I owned it. It was like an armoury that I could place around me when I felt threatened. And even though the anger was a negative force and it caused me all sorts of problems, there was a comforting certainty to my rage that made me feel safe.

I actually fought for my right to be and to stay angry. I ate my anger up like a steak dinner, and followed it down with sugary sweet puddings of self pity and melancholy. The abuse I experienced as a boy had become my safe haven as an adult. This was another revelation that changed my whole way of thinking. I could stay in that safe place, my 11-year-old self trapped inside the body of a grown man, and never move on. It was safe. No one expected much from me. *He was abused. He is depressed. He is compromised. Feel sorry for him. Don't place too much pressure on him. Certainly don't expect much from him.* I was like a ship that never left the harbour but, as the old saying goes, ships were not built to stay in the harbour.

I have a friend who had a breakdown. Her husband abused her. She'd had a hard life. Breakdown was the sorry result. She'd visited lots of healers, been before a plethora of mental health experts, and been counselled for uncountable hours, but her depression still remained.

I spoke with her and offered a solution, one that had worked for me and for many other victims of abuse. She was horrified that I could even suggest that she might be fixable. She was obviously very proud of the fact that no one could fix her. 'You don't even know what happened to me,' she shouted.

'I don't need to know what happened to you,' I replied. 'What happened is not important. What is important is the fact that I have a proven solution.'

I realised after an hour's chat with this lovely lady that she did not want a solution. She was happy being unhappy. She was content being on anti-depression tablets. She was not looking for a solution. Where she was may have been dire to me and you, but to her it was safe. It was reliable.

Another friend had an emotional breakdown after the suicide of his beautiful brother. This friend is a warrior, but the death jolted him. It took him so far outside his comfort that he ended up in a mental institution contemplating suicide himself. At his lowest ebb, when he was, what I can only describe as a shell, he realised that he was at a crossroads. He could move forward and out of the hospital—eventually back to good health. He could move up, to a place that he saw as death. Or he could slip backwards, disappearing into his small comfortable hospital room.

With great clarity and courage he told me that death was the most tempting of the three options. In his warped thinking, he thought of that as the end to his pain. His most fearful choice was to go forward, out of the hospital, and through his pain, where he could face his problems, meet them head on, and start collecting power. The second most tempting choice was to retreat to his sedated room at the hospital. It had a nice bed, a TV, and a CD player with his favourite tunes. His food was brought to him three times a day, along with tablets that helped him to sleep and potions that helped him to forget.

At the very point of taking his life, just when all hope had gone, my friend had a vision of his two children. Their faces appeared to him as though in a dream and he had a moment of clarity. He was able to see how his own death would affect their young lives.

He chose to live. He came out of the hospital, built himself back up to full strength, and is now one of the most powerful martial arts teachers in the world today. His message to his students is that they have a choice. Find someone to blame and slip into oblivion, or take responsibility and reap your power.

No matter where you are, no matter what you are, and no matter what happens in your life, you are always left with a choice.

When Boethius was on death row, he knew he had a choice. Victor Frankle had a choice, and Mandela too, in his Robin Island cell. When Mother Teresa was going through her dark night of the soul and her faith was compromised, she could easily have blamed God for abandoning her. She knew she had a choice, and she chose to collect power. Many years after the death of Frankle, Mother Teresa, and Boethius, the ghost of their power is so strong that it is still reverberating though out the world.

We all have choices. A warrior chooses the narrow path, the road less travelled. He chooses the straight gate.

Once you fully understood that you are always left with a choice, even when everything else seems to have been taken away, it becomes easier to take responsibility for your life and thus reclaim your power.

This whole chapter is about a warrior stepping up and taking control of his own world. This is a warrior's power base right here. When you take responsibility for your own existence, that existence becomes one of infinite possibilities.

So pen and paper to the ready. Get writing my friends and put the 'blame to shame.' By placing the blame onto paper, you expose it to the light. Blame is a shadow. It disempowers. And it is at its most potent when it is hidden.

Write them down. Bring them to the light. That which is exposed to light itself becomes light. Just the act of bringing it forward will weaken it. Remember, this is private. Don't be afraid of other people reading your words. This is between you and the page. Your mum doesn't need to see it if you don't want her to. Your dad does not have to read your words. You do not have to publish them in the local newspaper and expose them to the world. You can write them down and burn them afterwards. And if you feel afraid to write them down, all the more reason for you to get writing. The fear is not you. The fear is a shadow that fears the light of recognition. Write it down. Write it all down. The more juicy details the better. Be bold, be angry, be bitter, be jealous, be envious, be violently aggressive, be vitriolic, be murderous—but 'be' all of these things on paper.

Draw five columns. If you need more space, use one page for each column, more if necessary. Label them A, B, C, and D.

Write all of your blames under the A column.

Make the list extensive, be exhaustive. Let's have the whole jolly lot.

Under the B column, write down in great detail the feelings you are experiencing. Anger, sadness, melancholy, rage, self pity, vitriol, justified—whatever you are feeling, write it down until it is all spent.

Under the C column write down with brave honesty how these blames and these feelings have negatively affected your life.

How have they have affected your health? How have they have affected your relationships, your self esteem, and your career?

Write down every effect you can think of.

On column D, I want you to search your soul and see if you can find any positive things that have come from your blames, shames and feelings.

For instance, I felt as though my abuse as a child had blighted me in every way. I couldn't find any positives at all about the anger and the depression and low self esteem that I experienced as a result of being abused. On closer inspection however, I could see that I generated a lot of anger and energy from my low self esteem. When I used that energy as a driving force, I was able to convert it into a massive work ethic that enabled me to become a world class martial artist and write nearly 40 books. I converted the skills I learned into a saleable commodity, and made a lot of money from it.

Because I was abused and emotionally abandoned when I was 11 years old, I was left with a very low level of self worth. The anger this created enabled me to strive. I wanted to prove that I was worthy. I used my low self esteem to win a BAFTA. The prolific residue of energy left over from my abuse has fuelled every successful venture that I have ever taken on. People say to me, *how are you are so prolific?* I am so prolific because I was abused as a small boy. It fucked me, and left me like a burning mass of energy. I chose to use that gift to create a beautiful life for myself.

I know of a very famous footballer whose father was very abusive to him when he was a boy. His dad was a spiteful and mean man who chose to take his own problems out on his family. Knowing that his two sons were football fanatics, he would make them stand with their backs to the TV screen every Saturday afternoon when Match of the Day was on. If they turned to look at the game even once, he punished them.

The footballer grew up with very low self esteem because of this abuse. It caused him untold emotional pain. When he wrote *his* first list, similar to the one I am asking you to write here, it was filled with anger and shame. When he was asked to fill in column D to see if any good had come from his abuse, he was angry at even the suggestion. But when he examined his life, and looked carefully, honestly, and bravely at his achievements, he realised that at some level he had used this abuse and the anger. It had created in him a turbo drive, that not only saw him playing international football on Match of the Day, but also, after his playing days were over, working as a presenter on the programme.

As a child he did not have the power to face the TV screen against his father's will, but as an adult, he did have the power. Although he didn't fully realise it at the time, he used that power to great effect.

Write down all the areas where you have strived and achieved, despite your past—perhaps even because of your past.

Remember this. The power that you can draw from any dark episode will be wasted if you allow 'blame' to consume it. There is no power in list A, other than realising that blame is debilitating. There is no power in list B, other than to bring notice to how potent and potentially powerful your emotions are if you use them correctly, and how destructive they can be when left to their own devises. List C has potential power if you can recognise the destructive tendencies of power not controlled. List D is your power list. It shows you what a powerful person you really are. Not just despite your past abuses, but because of them.

Your ultimate aim should be to end up with just one list— the power list. This is the list of positive things you have created and are in the process of creating with your energy. Eventually there should be no blame list at all. It should fall below your game.

This all takes practice, but it is the job of a warrior to practice every day. So practice. When blame rears its ugly head, dissolve it and come back to yourself. If any of the negative emotions arise due to past trauma, present obstacles, or future dreads, do not engage them. Instead, drive the energy into solutions.

The best time to do this of course is *now*. Start immediately. Make this new philosophy your daily habit. The only time we truly have is the present moment, and you are compromised when you leave it. Do not be absent without leave from *the now*.

Unless it is for a specific reference or a powerful and positive visualisation, immerse yourself into the moment and make that your permanent abode.

Chapter Summary:

Through training and massive introspection the warrior stakes his claim by recognising that his power is his and his alone. He takes responsibility for his own universe, and never allows himself to look for cause outside of his own orbit.

You are your only friend, you are your only enemy.

Chapter Seven

†

A Warrior...
Lives in the Present

A warrior always lives in the present. He has to. He knows that living anywhere else is far too exhausting, and eats up energy at a rate of knots. Living today whilst trying to carry yesterday and negotiate tomorrow is to carry three times as much as you need.

A warrior likes to travel light, so he does not carry any such burden. He disciplines himself through daily practice to stay in the present, visiting past and future only for deliberate purpose. To live outside of the body with the mind flying off to past fears or idylls, or taking flights of imagined fancy into the near or far future, to dream of riches or dreaded anticipations, is not to live at all.

Most people are carrying small bundles of death around with them wherever they go. Old scripts, unprocessed life experience, suppressed and repressed anger, hurt and pain, unspoken grudges, and addictions, drag you down. This was the gist of the last chapter. Most people that are aware of these shadows or shades look to blame someone or something for their existence. When you do this, as we have already established, you place yourself into a posture of disempowerment. In doing so, you leave yourself vulnerable, not only to existing shadows, but also to new shadows that want to hitch a ride on your coattails or squat in your body and mind.

These ghosts are an abomination because they fill you with fear and block your natural flow of energy. They either re-direct your life force into damaging habits and addictions, or they create an energy-overload that, when unused, lead to clogs and clotting, and when mis-used, lead to addiction, violence, or dependency.

A warrior does not live in the past, though he might fleetingly re-visit historical experience as a reference point when current circumstance demands an empirical answer.

Unhappy in their present, many people transport themselves into fantastical future landscapes, living more in their projected tomorrows than in they do in the here and now. A warrior does not live in the future, although he will certainly goal-set and plan ahead. He may, if he is practised, even visit the future to prepare the ground for his arrival. But he does not live in the future until tomorrow arrives.

Mostly he will stay in the present moment, knowing that what he enjoys in the now is the result of what he did in yesterday's present moment. And what he sows in today's present he will reap in the harvest of tomorrow.

He knows therefore, that the past, the present, and the future are all in the same place, here and now. There is no purpose in being anywhere else. The way to gain maximum profit out of your life is to be present in your life at all times.

In terms of growth, the present moment is *the burn*. As I said earlier, if you want massive growth, then you need to get into the burn quickly and stay in the burn long. If the warrior visits the past or projects to the future, it is for a specific and profitable purpose only. He is there by design. He is not there by accident or against his own will. He will not be dragged back by dark remembrance or shot forward by excited or fearful anticipation.

To stay present, the warrior has to clear up any unfinished business. He has to lay to rest his old ghosts to stop them from haunting him and dragging him backward or forward, in and out of time. He does this by facing his fears on a daily basis, exposing his shadows in the process, and bringing them to the light. (For a 200-page treatise dedicated only to this subject, see my book *Hunting the Shadow*). He strengthens his concentration so he can hold the present moment, even when strong forces are trying to drag him forward or back. This muscular concentration (or attention) is developed with exercises in mindfulness and Zen—learning to hold the mind steady through the art of focus.

The biggest problem with present-moment living is that most people are unaware that they are not already doing it. You can't really change something if you are not aware of its existence. But the warning signs are there sure enough. When you find yourself harping back to your past, you are not living now. When you find that in your ever-present moment you are talking about or dreaming of a better future—yet doing nothing to make it so—you are not living now. If you are a fearful, stressed, worried or harried individual, it is because you have fallen out of the present moment. When you are stressed, it is because you are anxious about something in the past or the future—or both. Often we worry about our past actions catching up with us in the future, which creates a lot of fear.

When you are fearful, it is not the present moment that

scares you, because you are already there. It is the future that you fear. And yet, the future does not even exist. We live in a continual past/present/future moment, where tomorrow does not yet exist, and yesterday is but a ghost. They have no reality. We project to the past and the future, usually against our own will, because we have not trained the mind to stay present.

The poet Milton said that the mind is its own place. It can make a heaven out of hell and a hell out of heaven. The mind *is* its own place, and if you train it to stay present, you can make your world a perpetual heaven on earth. When you think about it logically, there is nothing outside of the mind to fear. It is the world we create inside with our mind that we need to deal with.

Returning to what I said earlier, everything comes back to *you*. You are the source. You are your own beginning and your own end. You are the cause of all your own happiness and the root to all your own pain. You are your success and you are your failure. Most of the time, success and failure are just perceptions. If someone says you are honourable and gives you a title, it makes you happy and proud. If the same people threaten to take it away again, suddenly you are sad and depressed, even suicidal.

A very famous chef in France was honoured with three Michelin Stars for his restaurants. It made him very happy—at first, anyway. It also made him proud, famous and very rich. He was obviously an incredibly gifted chef with or without these three stars. But once he had the Michelin badge, he started to feel as though, like Samson minus the locks, he would be powerless without them.

Even though this was not true in fact, it was true in his mind, so it became his reality. He spent most of his time *out of time*, projecting into the future where he imagined and dreaded that he might have his three stars taken from him. He became so anxious that he took his own life. The threat of someone else's negative opinion of his work in the future was so threatening to him, that killing himself felt an easier option.

This is how most people spend most of their lives. They worry about the future (it doesn't exist), and lament over the past (it doesn't exist), never fully living in the now.

I am patently aware of the fact that 'live now' is a cliché thrown around like some great social panacea. You see it on coffee cups and emblazoned across the front of tee-shirts. People say it to you as though 'staying present' is as simple as putting an extra blanket on the bed when it gets cold. I have to say that to my mind *it is* a great panacea, and deserves to be lauded on tee-shirts and coffee mugs. But it is patronizing when people tell you to do it as though it is as easy as taking a pill. Especially so, when you know that the person telling you is not living the message themselves. The overweight life coach comes to mind.

What I will tell you is that living in the present is a skill you will need to train your whole life to acquire, and you may never fully master it. Just the pursuit of it, however, is an exhilarating challenge, one that I recommend to anyone in search of a braver life. The mere fact that you rarely meet a mind master tells you that the skill is as elusive as it is mysterious. It also tells you that the skill is worth a lifetime of study, because it is so rare.

The methods of practice are so obvious that most people miss them. Sometime they even trip over them, and then get up and walk away as though nothing happened. They don't see the truth because it is so obvious. *The truth hidden in plain sight*, as I like to say.

In martial arts, people always ask me how to become a great fighter. I tell them that the best way to become a great fighter is to fight. There are systems that you can train in and there are arts you can follow, but basically a fighter fights.

The Samurai warrior Muhashi (or *the serial killer* Muhashi, as my wife likes to describe him), wanted to be a warrior. He acquired a sword and at the age of 14, fought his first duel, killing a grown man. He then spent most of the rest of his life going from one battleground to the next, fighting and perfecting the art of fighting.

Fighters fight. That is how they get good at it. I spent 10 years training in martial arts before I realised that, even as a second-dan in karate, with years of study under my belt, I was still scared and I could not fight. I felt like a fraud. On the outside I looked the part, but underneath I knew I was not a fighter.

My self-knowing served me well—you might say that it saved me. Living a lie created a lot of depression in me, and as a young man it took its toll. Eventually I did the one thing that I had secretly been avoiding my whole life: I went out and I faced my fears. For me, this meant becoming a nightclub bouncer in the city of Coventry. For those who have read my work before, this is old news so I will not go into it again. Suffice it to say, I became a fighter by fighting. (Please refer to my book *Watch My Back* for a 500-page detail on the matter).

When people ask me about becoming a writer, the same advice applies: A writer writes. That is how he gets good at writing. Courses and degrees and study can help. They can direct you, sharpen you, finesse you. But ultimately a writer writes, a director directs, a runner runs, and a climber climbs.

A mountain climber wrote to me once with a question about self defence. He wanted to know if I thought an instructor with no fighting experience could teach others to defend themselves in a real fight. I asked him a question in response: *Could someone who practices mountain climbing in a sports hall teach you to ascend a rock face in the Himalayas?*

He got my point immediately.

If you want to excel at staying present, if you want to be a master at controlling your mad-monkey mind, if you want powerful attention, then practice staying present. Practice staying in the here and now. Every time your mind wanders backward or forward against your own will, practice holding it firm.

How do you get good at lifting weights? By lifting weights of course. You can develop different techniques in the gym, perfect different grips and stances to help you, but ultimately you get good at lifting weights by lifting weights. By doing the thing that you want to be good at a lot, you get good at it. That is the fast track.

In terms of the mind, the weights that you need to lift are

the everyday situations that try to drag you back and forward in time. Be a time traveller if that is your intention, but do not be a traveller in time against your own will.

How often are you projected violently into the future by the news bulletins and provocative tabloid headlines that proclaim the end of the world, or at least another economic downturn? How often are you dragged into your dark past by a friend or a family member (or even your own untrained mind), reminding you of your past misdemeanours, your historical bad deeds, or your shameful mistakes? And is there a single day of the week where you are not hooked out of the present moment by the fantastical (and false) promises of the lottery fortune, the X-factor fame, or the thought of shagging some semi-clad soap star on front of a monthly-gossip/porn magazine?

There are opportunities all day and every day to practice. The ordinary life is the arena. You do not have to take yourself off somewhere to practice when you are already in the very middle of the best practice a man could ask for. You can go off to a fancy retreat if you really want to. You can hug trees, chant until you're hoarse, and whirl dervishly until you are dizzy-sick. But my philosophy is this. If you want to be a good wrestler, why not just get your leotard on and wrestle?

Call me a raving genius, but it all seems so obvious. I could show you a plethora of exercises and meditations that might help, but if I'm being honest, there is no substitute for the ordinariness of the every day. There are fantastic challenges right under your nose as we speak. Let me throw a few at you as a quick example.

1)   Don't gossip. Don't be tempted.

It is harder than climbing Everest and fewer people have achieved it. Gossip yanks you out of the present moment in a heartbeat.

2)   Don't talk or think about the past for a week.

See how hard it is to not go backward. The very act of resisting the urge to talk or think, good or bad, about the past, is an exercise in cerebral weightlifting.

3)   Don't talk or think about the future for a week.

Try it and see how many times you find yourself projecting to your next meal, your next day off work, your next holiday, or your monthly pay day. You'll be amazed at how often you are out of your body.

4)   Have a day without a wish.

Do you know how many people spend their entire life wishing they were living a different life? More than you can shake a stick at (and that is a lot of people). The moment you engage in wishing, you are out of your body, you are out of time, and you are out of control. Have a break. Resist. Grow your attention.

5) Don't worry for an hour.

If an hour is too much to start with, try 10 minutes and build up.

How often have you heard people say, 'don't worry' when they find out you have things on your mind. You find yourself thinking ,'I'd love to not worry—but *how*?!'

Pulling your mind from a worrying thought feels like trying to pull yourself out of an oceanic current, even strong swimmers struggle to do it. Like everything else of any worth it takes practice, it takes developed strength, and it takes technique. The best way to develop this powerful triune is to place yourself before the best opponents out there and practice.

As I said at the beginning of this section, the best opponents are the ones you face every day, five of which I have just listed here. The technique and the strength are all grown in the arena. The world is your garden, and the ordinary challenges that everyone tries to avoid are the fertiliser.

» Warrior Practices:

I have already alluded to some of the practices for this chapter, certainly the most important ones. But as an aside, I would like to invite you now to follow your attention over the period of a day. Be aware of how many times your mind wanders in and out of the present moment. No need to make any notes (unless you want to). To notice is enough for now.

Once you realise how often you are out of the present you will be able to start doing something about it.

The exercises mentioned in the last section (the list of five), can be undertaken in the normal span of a day. This is exciting, because it will enable you to strengthen your concentration so you can hold your mind in place.

Other exercises that can help develop your attention and give it more muscularity are as listed below.

» Seated meditation

I will keep it basic, because basic is potent. Find a quiet spot. Sit with your legs crossed and back straight. Close your eyes and follow your breathing. Lock your attention on your breathing. There is only this one thing to do, so there is nothing to remember. Just follow the breathing. When your attention wanders, bring it back. The act of bringing the attention back to the breath is *resistance training* for the attention. If you can control the attention, you can control everything else. Twenty minutes twice a day is a good start.

» Moving meditation

When you are walking, follow the sound and the feel and the rhythm of your feet as they hit the floor. Deliberately slow the walk down. Keep your attention locked on nothing but your feet. This works best if you are in a park, or on a country lane. Don't do it if you think there is a danger of walking into something. Your mind will want to wander away from the feet. Bring it back. It will try to engage you in talk. Bring it back. The mind will try and take you to a million dark or exotic places. Bring it back. Every time you bring the mind back to the feet against its will, you will develop strength and technique. You will become the top dog.

» Working meditation

This is my favourite because it means that, if we are diligent, we can practice meditation eight hours a day. Some of you, especially if you are engaged in jobs that you love, will already be doing this without knowing. And how can you not get good if you are practicing eight hours a day?

The key with working meditation is to keep your focus

entirely on what you are doing. If you are painting a fence, paint the fence, nothing else. Don't paint a fence and day dream out of your body to your next holiday.

When the mind gets into the grove of doing a job, any job, even just driving the car, it will quickly get the hang of it. Once mastered, it will be able to do the job and think a million things at the same time. Paint the fence. When the mind wanders away to other things, fears, stresses, dreams, partners, etc., bring it back. Every time it drifts, bring the attention back to the fence. Stay present. Notice the paint as it spreads across the wood, the bristles of the brush, the texture of the paint, the smell. Go into every detail of your job, and resist the temptation of allowing your mind to drift.

Like any muscle, the mind will weaken if you do not train it. Whether you are painting the fence or building a wall, keep the attention locked on the job in hand and in the present moment.

» Physical and mental archery

To shoot an arrow straight takes great concentration. Great concentration is simply the attention held on one object. Many of the ancient Japanese samurai practiced bow, because it strengthened their attention. In the book *Shogun*, the author James Clavelle says that to think bad thoughts is really the easiest thing in the world. They just wander into the untrained mind all on their own. Often they wreak havoc. To think good thoughts, however, requires effort. Therefore, you should train your mind to dwell on the beauty of nature, raindrops hitting the roof, birds singing, even listening for silence, and allow it to envelop you.

Accessing your attention and then training your attention is vital if you want to have control of your mind and stay in the present moment. It is also important that you know the difference between your sight and your attention. They are two different things. Although the attention is often directed by the eyes, it isn't exclusive to the eyes.

Try this little experiment and you will see what I mean. Choose an object in front of you and look directly at it. Don't allow your eyes to move in their sockets. Now, with the eyes perfectly still, take your inner attention to the big toe on your right foot. Feel the toe with your mind. You are looking forward with your outer eye, and you are looking inward with your inner eye—your attention.

Try it again. Keep your eyes ahead. Don't move them. Take your attention this time to someone you love, your wife, husband, mother, father, anyone. Your eyes are locked ahead, held firmly on the object of choice, but your attention is in another place, out of your body, with your loved one. This is just a small exercise to help you see where your sight and your attention separate, how they are very different, and why they sometimes work together, but more often, apart. The thing to remember is that both the eyes and the attention are under your control, even if at the moment you have not developed the muscle or skill or technique to master that control.

What you are doing here by deliberately sending your gaze and your attention in two different directions at the same time is what's happening to most people all the time, against their will and without their knowledge. Developing control of the attention is your way of getting control back again so you can direct where your attention is and is not.

Archery is a very good way of mastering the attention. It takes a great deal of concentration to hold, not only your eyes, but also your concentration on the target. There is nothing more to say on archery that is not better demonstrated by actually having a go at it yourself. So have a go.

Inner archery is the same as outer archery, but without the physicality. With the inner game, you shoot at the target in your mind's eye with a virtual bow and arrows. Whilst the physical workout is lacking from this exercise, it is still very good for isolating the attention.

Sit somewhere quiet. Make sure you will not be disturbed by phones or family. Close your eyes, and imagine a straw target one hundred yards ahead of you in a field. See your bow and your arrow by your side, ready to use. Pick the bow up, feel the wood in your hand, feel how tight the string is. Take an arrow, feel its weight, load it onto the bow, and try to make it feel as real as possible. Draw the bow, eyes and attention on the target, and fire. Watch the arrow as it flies through the air into the centre of the straw target. The more real you can make this in your mind, the more benefit you will get from the practice. It might seem to be little more than an exercise in visualisation, but if you do it properly it is much more. You can make it so visceral that it will actually feel real.

Once you get the hang of it, staying present and living in the now will become a good habit. Everything you do, from washing the car to writing your opus, will be an exercise in Zen. When I first started learning the warrior arts, I used to get perplexed. Should I run today or should I hit the bag? Should I do yoga or qigong? Will a walk in the park be best for my mind training or a seated meditation with chant? It all became very stressful because I wanted to do everything every day. I was worried that if I didn't do all the exercises, or certainly if I didn't do the right exercise, I would be missing out on my development. I later realized to my delight that anything can be meditative, and everything can be meditative. You can train your mind just as easy with a paint brush in your back garden as you can with a gong in a Buddhist temple.

Chapter Summary.

This chapter is about understanding how, with a clear, flowing, congruent body, developed by staying in the present with a muscular attention, you can access massive power, and use that power to create prolifically. There is nothing you cannot achieve if you can master the mind.

Chapter Eight

✝

A WARRIOR...
IS A RESPONSIBLE PARENT

The legendary self-help guru Zig Ziggler was visiting a prison in America many years ago, passing on his wisdom to folk that were down on their luck. One troubled inmate asked him how he managed to becomes so successful. Zig told him, *When I was a boy my father always said that I'd be successful and rich. He drilled it into me....I never let him down.* The prisoner smiled sadly and said, *My dad always said I'd be a con and end up in jail. He drilled that into me too....I guess that I never let him down either.*

You might be wondering why I have included a chapter on parenting in a book about becoming a warrior. Hopefully this first story might have given you some indication as to my intent. Kids are our future. We are their guardians. From the moment they are born, we are entrusted with preparing them to live in the world. For the first and most important years of their lives we are their only teachers. It is our very strong impressions during that small window of opportunity that determine how successful they will become.

Every kid wants their parent to be a warrior, don't they? Kids go to the cinema every week to watch films about heroes. They all want to be brave wizards like Harry, or adventurous little fishes like Nemo. So what better example is there to offer your child than to unfold your own life as a warrior, a breathing example of how to live right?

Becoming a parent is a life-altering event. I know, I have four children, and it changed me forever. (It took me ages to get my figure back). As parents, we become the principle influence of a new life, a huge responsibility, and that authority starts from the moment of conception. *Conception*

(unless they regret the

New science tells us that everything affects everything. When a bird lands in a tree, the whole world changes. If this is true, and personal experience tells me that it is, then who we are, where we are, and how we live, will have a profound and enduring impact on our growing child. This is true even during the nine months of pregnancy, *and* the

• 176 •

first five years of life when the infant brain is still plastic and highly susceptible to strong impressions. This is why it is imperative to be a warrior, to live honestly, healthily and with great integrity. What you are is what you teach.

This is exciting because we get the chance to marinate our offspring in the most delicious and advantageous conditions. It is also frightening because, as the poet Larkin so succinctly suggested, if we get it wrong, we might just fuck our kids up.

If you want your child to be studious, be studious yourself. Let him see you reading, have books lying around the house. In fact if you are able to, have your own library. If you want your child to grow into a healthy adult, teach with your actions. Do not be three stone overweight, smoking cigarettes, and expect to offer yourself as a congruent role model. You are fat and unhealthy. A good role model you are not. It doesn't mean you don't love your kids. It just means that as a messenger to the most important people in the world, you are greatly lacking.

I watched a lady on the news just last week saying how she lied about where she lived, so that she could get her children into a better school. She was proud of it, and said she would do it again. In so doing, she negated their fundamental schooling in one fell swoop by teaching them on daytime television that lying is acceptable.

If you fiddle your taxes, don't evangelise to your kids on the merits of honesty and integrity. You are a liar and a thief. You have no right to talk of virtues if yours are so easily sold. If you want them to be powerful, show them power in your everyday life. If you want them to be brave, don't teach them to be cowards by living and putting up with abusive partners.

I have a friend who hides behind the settee every time her abusive ex knocks on the door to see their child. He has threatened her life on many occasions and she is terrified of him. She has every right to take unsupervised custody away from her ex, but she is too scared to apply for it, fearing he will threaten her again. She does not fill in the forms or book her day in court, even though the police and social workers have assured her of their full protection.

Instead, she continues to hide behind the settee every time she hears a knock, in case it's him. You only have to spend five minutes in their company to see that she adores her son. His estranged father says he loves him too, but he hardly, if ever, sees the boy. And when he does see his son, he smokes drugs around him, talks violently, and is derogatory towards women. My friend says that her son's welfare is her main priority, and yet she continues to teach him, unconsciously, how to live a scared life by not standing up for her rights. She was not fully aware of how impressionable her 4-year-old was. In fact, it was not until it was pointed out that her misguided attempts to protect her son were, in fact, teaching him how be fearful, that she actually started to live like a warrior.

If you want your kids to be brave, you have to live brave. That is the only lesson that they are going to heed. If you want them to exercise, make sure *you* exercise.

I don't care who you vote for. I have no interest in your church or your denomination. How much you earn says nothing to me. (I know millionaire drug dealers and I know crooked billionaire business men). Where you live and holiday and what you drive does not even get my attention. What I am interested in is who you are. Are you full of virtue, or are you living a lie and calling it truth? What you are is what you teach your children. And if what you say is not congruent with what you are then your words are wasted, like piss in the face of a tsunami.

Because it is based on common sense, there is little to say in this chapter that is not completely obvious.

» Warrior Practices:

A lot of people act unconsciously with their children. They automatically do and say things without realising the impact their words and actions are having. The warrior practice in this chapter is to closely examine your relationship with your children. Here are a few questions I'd like you to consider:

» Are you patient?

It is awful if your children are walking around on eggshells because you are impatient with them. It will develop in them an underlying anxiety they may never lose. My best friend said that when she was a child, her father was a very impatient man with a hair-trigger temper. Although she loves him dearly, she still gets adrenalin when she is around him, even though she is now 40 years old.

Don't inflict this on your children. Don't inflict it on yourself. Impatience is stress underlying, and stress will eventually kill you. Be patient, be consummately patient, and slow everything down for you and for your child. Make their time with you a pleasure. Train them to love being with you. Be a sage to your child.

or blame them for their father's heart condition

» Are you in shape?

If you want your children to be in shape, be in shape yourself. It is lazy and ignorant and naive to talk fitness when kids are really only going to be taught with their eyes. If they see you fit, then your message is 10 times more powerful. It is good for your child if you are in shape. It is good for you. A small investment in your own fitness everyday will bring you and your child great dividends.

» Are you living your dream?

I often to talks at schools, universities, and colleges where the teachers are using only words to teach—and many of them do not use the right words. The right words are, *You can achieve anything. You can live the dream.* They don't use these words because secretly they don't believe them. Many of the teachers are not living their own dreams, so why are they going to tell the kids they can live theirs?

A child's first teacher is their parents, so it is important that they see you living the dream, *your* dream, whatever that might be. If not living the dream, then you should at least be pursuing the dream. Bring them up on the lottery and X-Factor and you are weaning them on impotence. You are telling them that life is about luck, when actually that is not true. Life is about striving and creating your dream. I see friends living lives they hate, trying to tell their kids they can live lives that they love. There is no congruence, just a lie. It may indeed be a well-intentioned lie, but a lie all the same. Live your dream, and be a living example to your child that they can live theirs.

» Be present:

I have written a whole chapter on presence and its importance. It is equally important here. Be present with your kids.

When you are with your kids, are you really with them? Or are you multi-tasking their time away? Are you fitting other jobs around the time you have with them? Are you taking them to the pub with you just so you can go to the pub? Are you with them, but taking business calls for half the time? Are you there in body, but somewhere else in spirit?

I think it is better to either be with your kids and give them your full attention, or don't be with them at all. Kids are sensitive, just like the rest of us. They know when you are not present. So switch your phone off for an hour, leave your laptop at the office, turn the TV off, and spend proper time with them.

I work from home, so when my kids were growing up they were aware of me working. I explained the situation to them so they knew I was not working their time away. During the school holidays, when the kids were off, I'd get up extra early to work. I got half a day in by the time my kids climbed out of bed. This left me with lots of time to dedicate to them. When they were home in the day, I'd work an hour on and thirty minutes off. I'd say to my lad, *Come and fetch me in an hour*. I'd do my work, and in an hour's time he'd come for me and we'd play pool for half an hour. Then I'd go back to my work and say to my son, *Come and get me in an hour again*. And we'd do that throughout the day.

Your children are not young for long, and the time will fly, believe me. Make the changes sooner rather than later.

» Watch your language.

Do you use negative words like 'you're stupid' or 'you'll never do anything with your life,' or 'you're lazy?' People use the most inappropriate words and phrases with their kids all the time without realising their significance. When a child is young, the brain is still plastic and very easily influenced. If you tell a child enough times they are 'useless,' eventually you will not have to tell them at all, they will tell themselves.

Think of your child's brain as being like the hardware on a computer. You are responsible for the software. What you say, what you do, and what they see, hear, and intuit, will all go on the hard drive. And what you programme in will be there for life. It will be really hard to erase later, when your impressions are not making the impression you intended.

I was told rather harshly when I was young that I was not a writer, and I would never be a writer. I was told that my brother was a writer, but I was not. I went on to defy that parental projection only because I studied the psyche and taught myself how to clean the virus from my hard drive.

But I have to tell you, it created a crippling insecurity in me for many years, and caused me untold pain. I know very few people today who are not still suffering the insecurities and pain of the early software that their parents programmed in. Very few people are ever able to take the virus off again once it is on.

So my advice is this. Be very careful not to say, do, or be anything that you don't want on your child's hard drive. Fill them with love, train them in compassion and patience, expose them to all the beautiful things in life. There are a lot of them out there.

Or, tell them their head is full of shit like they are 8

Do not put shit in, because if you do, you will get shit out.

Those are just a few ideas to work on. You'll have many bad examples of what not to do from your own childhood. Most of us do—even though I'm sure that in most cases our parents were only doing what they thought was right.

Chapter Summary:

In this day and in this age, with the abundance of information available to us, we should at least have learned better than to follow the errors of our forebears. Let us not make the same mistakes as those that went before us.

This chapter is about honest vigilance, identifying the areas where our actions are not constructive, and then changing them. It is about learning from our own back-story—good and bad—so that we can better prepare our kids for a challenging new world.

We teach best with our actions, so be your gospel. Be a warrior.

Chapter Nine

†

A Warrior is...
Balanced

It would be easy (and quite understandable) to get this far into the book and think, *Crikey there is a lot to do.* Of course you would be quite right; there is always a lot to do. If you want to make the best of this short, earthly sojourn then there is much to squeeze into a relatively short span.

Ours is an exciting time to be alive. Actually, history suggests that every era was an exciting time to be alive. Good or bad, there is always something to do and there is always something to learn. But just because there is a lot to get through in your allotted life span, should not take away from the fact that you still need to be balanced. We must all work hard to achieve our dreams, and our study and learning will probably never end. This doesn't mean you can't have a great time as well. You still need time to play hard and rest hard. In fact, the play/rest portions of your life are no less important than the work section.

Often, when people realise that they can achieve anything, they start working like a maniac and never let up. This eventually affects their health and their relationships. Without balance, life can be pretty dull. The ideal scenario is that you place yourself into an employ that you love, so the work and the rest and the play start to intermingle. Life really can be bliss when you hit this centre.

I have been in this space for the last 15 or 20 years. I realised early on in my life that I did not want to work in a real job. I always wanted to live the dream. At about the age of 30, after working for 15 years in a plethora of menial and manual jobs—from carrying a hod on a building site, to making pizza in an Italian restaurant, to working in nightclubs as a bouncer—I gave up conventional employment and became a full time martial arts instructor.

Obviously I'd invested many years training myself to the level where this was a possibility. I didn't just give up my job and try to make a living at something I was not expert in. As a full-time trainer, I taught people martial skills every day, privately in classes, and later in courses. The rest of the time

I spent training myself, and increasing my own skills so that my teaching platform could grow bigger and bigger.

It was bliss I have to tell you. Teaching classes and training. No clocking in and clocking out. No one looking over my shoulder, and no more relying on other people to find and set my wage. There were no negotiations every year to fight for a 5 percent wage rise. If I wanted more money, I just worked harder at increasing my skills to attract more students.

I vividly remember one day walking around my local area posting 5,000 leaflets to advertise my martial arts club. I treated it like a working day. I posted leaflets for two hours, took a tea break, then posted for another two hours, and stopped for some dinner. I spent two more hours at the letter boxes in the afternoon, and then I stopped again for tea. After two more satisfying hours of letter posting in the afternoon, I went home.

I felt so free doing what I wanted, when I wanted, and how I wanted. The more leaflets I posted, the more benefit I got. The more I trained and honed my skills, the more students I attracted. Everything I did came directly back to me. There were no middle men taking their cut, just me, my work, and my reward. There was no better feeling in the world than knowing that the more I trained and the better I got at my art, the more money I would earn. It was a great incentive I have to tell you. But better than all that was the fact that I was doing something I loved. My training was my job. For the first time ever, I felt as though I was living my life as a warrior. It was the most gratifying feeling.

This of course is the ideal. Few people are currently in this space—but they could be if they wanted to. My advice is that if you are not already in your nirvana, then start working toward it. What you see in your mind's eye, your dream life, is there already waiting for you. It is a definite possibility. Many thousands of people are already doing it, and a lot of them (as you know), are not as competent as you. If *they* can, *you* can.

George Hackenschmidt, a hero of mine, was a real warrior. He was a man born in humble origins at the end of the late 1900s. He went on to become a gentle, articulate, multi-lingual world champion weightlifter and wrestler, who stole the hearts of Britain before the Great War. He was an amazing physical specimen who developed his brain to match his brawn. He was also a great philanthropist and a lover of humankind. In short, he was complete; a man of balance. He was and he is a great example of what a true warrior should be, and a great example of what we can all become if we invest in ourselves.

The majority of us are not warriors. In fact, contemporary man is largely out of balance. He is either mentally astute, but physically weak, or he is Atlas on the outside and witless on the in. There is a fine balance that can be found between these two polar opposites, where we are both physical and cerebral; where our bodies are healthy and our mind is open and fertile; where we can run a marathon or do a hard gym session whilst quoting Ghandi or Gurdjieff; where we are at once deliciously buff and beautifully articulate.

The Japanese Samurai were great advocates of this rare balance. Whilst they mastered the art of lethal swordplay to serve them in the theatre of war—the men *and* the women—also honed their skills in flower arranging, tea ceremonies, and calligraphy as a necessary counter balance.

Ultimately their aim was to serve society, and to do that effectively they needed much more than just skill with a sword. They developed themselves to physical perfection, while nurturing a taste for art and culture, honing their fiscal and economic skills, and developing a mastery of their environment. In short, they developed every facet of themselves so they became as comfortable on the battlefield as in the boardroom.

The amazing thing is, if you make your passion your employ, you will be able to do this as a part of your working day.

To be a great teacher and writer, a big part of my job is to improve myself daily. Every day as a part of my work, I train and study to enhance my skills, sharpening what I have already forged whist building up the areas that are underdeveloped.

It seems to me that we have forgotten how exciting the world is, how much potential there is out there to grow and develop. In the lower sink areas of society, intellectual ignorance is almost celebrated, and an educated man is both reviled and feared. Those with a physical bent, but with no matching articulation, are looked down upon like a cattle class, to be steered and poked by those with political and fiscal clout. In many of the so-called higher echelons, man has completely lost contact with his physical and moral being all together, and has ended up looking like a large self-serving brain balancing on a plate of jelly.

Balance is not only imperative, it is also very exciting. We have so much potential we are not using, it is almost a sin. Our brains are crying out to be developed. The hardware is already in place, waiting for us to get to work. We are given the most amazing machine (our brain and our body), yet sadly, most people go to their graves never having sung their best song. We are sitting on a lottery ticket that most never cash.

It is never too late to start, as long as we use the present moment, right now, as our launch pad. Don't put it off until tomorrow, because that always stinks of delay. Delay is just another way of never actually starting in the first place.

As a warrior you should be rounded. It is not enough to be physically developed or intellectually astute. Being good in business, but terrible in personal relationships, is not advised either.

Here are some of the important areas you should look into developing, if you haven't already started.

1) Physicality.

Start with the physical body, because everything we experience we experience through the body. We have already looked at this in previous chapters.

2) Palate.

Master your palate—what you eat, what you drink, what you read, who you listen to and watch, your influences and your environment. Bring them all under your control.

3) Psychology.

I studied to the level of a master's degree in psychology so I could better understand my on workings. I have written several books on the subject, just to underline and cement this understanding. In fact, my master's thesis is published in a book called *StressBuster*. Whilst I am not saying that you need to do a master's, I am suggesting that you get at least a working knowledge of the mind. You'll be amazed at what a difference it makes.

4) Physiology.

Learn about the workings of the internal body, specifically the adrenals and their relationship with the stress response. Once you have a basic understanding of the internal schematic, how digestion works, the function of the brain, the right and wrong foods for your body, you will be able to change your perception of the machine we call a body.

Whilst you still see yourself as your body, you will always live under the dominion of fear, because you will forever live in dread of your body going wrong. Once you understand that the body is a machine, a vehicle built to take us through life, you start to treat it differently. Certainly you will start to treat it better. Like a precision motor, you will want to put the very best fuel into it. You will feel compelled to maintain it (like any vehicle that is taking you on a long journey), and you will want to get the very best out of it at all times.

Most people are dictated to by fear, but only because they do not understand fear. Once you see fear as a normal bodily reaction, your vehicle's way of preparing you for potential danger, you stop taking it all so personally. If a red light comes on in your car indicating you need oil, you don't fly off into a panic. You simply recognise that your car is showing you the state of play. If you have any sense at all you heed the warning and you top up the oil in the engine.

Similarly, when you feel fear, it is the body's way of indicating that something (internally or externally) needs attention. If you listen and don't panic, you can deal with that situation calmly and move on. We are so accustomed to panicking when the red light of fear comes on that we end up frightened to live. Fear is what keeps ordinary people imprisoned. That is why they say that fear is the friend of extraordinary people.

5) Sociology.

Study how people interact with each other. Study how you interact with the world and how you react with yourself. You have a relationship with every person on the planet. At some level everything connects. You also have a social relationship with yourself. You communicate with your body with every ingestion: food, drink, information, environment, and influences. Everything that enters you becomes a part of you. First it is translated into chemicals, and then it is converted into flesh. When they say you are your influences, they mean it literally. If you think this is not true, see how your body talks to you when you walk through, or live in, a dangerous area. It will talk to you about danger and death. See what your body tells you when you eat too much, drink excessively, or take drugs. If not at the time of consumption, it will certainly talk to you the next day of illness and threat.

Listen to your body's alarm bells ring out when you find yourself in the wrong company, talking with negative people. See how it sings when you are in the company of a spiritual person, or when you read an inspirational book or quote.

You also interrelate with yourself. Your internal dialogue is firing off instructions all day, every day. Most often the instructions are not positive, because, generally speaking, the input of information for the majority of people is not positive. Most of the time people are talking to themselves about what they don't have, what they can't make happen, and about how lost they feel.

If you listen carefully to your own internal voice, you will hear its usual range—anything from confusion (*I don't know what I am doing*), to anger (*I hate her/him/them*), right through to despair (*I can't do this anymore*).

There will be lots of other dialogue too, mundane things, like what you fancy for dinner, or deciding what clothes to wear on a night out. The majority of the chatter will be either neutral or negative. The negative voices tend to get stronger and clearer as you venture outside of your comfort zone. There, the chatter will become more fearful, often insidious, reminding you of how *useless you are*, how *out of your depth you feel*, and that *you can't cope*.

Understanding the power potential in your social connections is important. If you are not aware of your potential, and if you are not aware that most of your social interactions are taking you away from your potential, then there is little you can do about it.

Can you imagine how hard it would be to succeed in any endeavour if you had someone telling to you 24 hours a day that you are useless and you will never succeed? It would be nearly impossible. Now reverse the equation. Imagine that you had people around you all day every day, on call, 24/7 telling you what an amazing, beautiful, wonderful, powerful, successful person you are. Imagine if you had a voice or voices that instructed, guided, trained, helped, and loved you. Can you imagine having that with you all the time? How wonderful. But that is what you have access to right here and right now. The voices just need to be trained. You need to instruct them.

If the voices are external (other people), and they are negative, change them for voices that are positive. It is within your power to do that. Living as a warrior means developing the courage to tell people straight when you don't like the way they speak to you. They might not like your honesty, but they will think twice about talking down to you the next time.

Your internal voice often becomes an extension of the voices you hear around you every day, and the voices you have heard around you your entire life. Their words become your script. Notice when the internal critic starts. Focus on the voice without actually engaging it. The very act of noticing the inner opponent will weaken it. The internal voice feeds off you. If you listen and you buy into its negative sales talk, it will grow stronger. If, however, you do not buy the spiel, it will eventually atrophy. As I said earlier, what you pay attention to will grow. What you take attention away from will shrink.

6) Economical—the money issue.

Understanding economy is a vital part of the warrior's path. Understanding money and the flow of capital is essential when you consider what an important role it plays in the world.

Money is a touchy subject, and this is part of the problem. Money topics should not be any more sensitive than talking about the weather. My feeling is, the more we talk about it the less of an issue it will be. Some people think that lucre is as filthy as the muck it is said to come from, and that the gates of heaven are welded shut to those who hold it. Their belief is that anyone earning above the minimum wage must be either as crooked as a pirate's hook or dirty-greedy-bad.

Others still are mad-afraid of cold hard cash. Their hearts fear its seducing ways. Money is said to be the very seat of power, and of course power corrupts just as 'absolute power corrupts absolutely.'

Then there are those that simply have a limited understanding of money—what money means, what it represents, and how or where to get more of it. They only know that they have very little in their wallet and their bank account. They believe their lack of money separates them from the freedom they crave.

The rarer few know that money is neither good nor bad, it is just numbers on a balance sheet that the skilled learn to move around. In its more material manifestation, it comes as a paper and metal IOU, a tool (made from energy) that we use to barter with. Those wise enough to separate themselves from the hysterical, primitive, and 'mystical' emotionality of cash educate themselves in the fiscal way and study economics. They build a solid infrastructure of virtue so they can carry the weighty responsibility that having money demands. They learn to master its shape and distribution, and make it labour for them in a way that profits everyone.

The very best way to make money work for you is to make it work for everyone.

My experience and my instinct and my intellect tell me that money in and of itself can be neither good nor bad. It is an inanimate object. It is the hand of man that determines its intent.

My senses also tell me that lucre could not possibly be filthy. Never. It can be used by people whose intentions are filthy, but in and of itself it cannot be anything other than what it is.

People who earn a lot of money are fundamentally no different really from people who earn none at all. They are just people. What they do with their position is what determines who and what they are. I know very good people and very bad people who are rich. Equally, I know very good and very bad people who are fiscally poor.

Ultimately, money is just one of the shapes we make with our energy. Our energy, according to science, comes directly from the stars , so we all have access to the same amount of it.

I find this very exciting. I get to access the same raw material as Bill Gates and Mother Teresa, Richard Branson and Mahatma Gandhi. We all have the same amount of potential energy available to us and that amount is infinite. The more we take from it the more there is. What we do with that energy, the shapes we make with it, is entirely up to us.

The informed take energy and use it to develop skills and products, which they then sell on the open market. The wise develop skills and products that serve the multitude, putting their manifestations in high demand. If we are industrious, as we are meant to be, then we use our energy to make ourselves into market leaders. That makes our skills and products sought around the globe.

I must stipulate here that we are talking about just one of the manifestations of energy—there are many more. In my experience, the principle holds true with them all. If you have information that can help people, but choose not to share it, that is the equivalent of burying your talent in the ground. What little you have will be taken away from you. Therefore, you must share it. Give it out. Let the world have what you know, and when you do, you will be given more.

One of the main reasons I choose to write my learning down and put it out into the world, is because I know that more will not be given to me until I pass on what I have. You have to continually make room for the new.

It is said that the wise man has to give over his traveler's notes before he can become a sage. If you have skills, pass those skills on to others abundantly, and you will make room for a higher level of skill. If you have skills and choose to guard them like a jealous husband, even the small amount of expertise you have will eventually diminish. This works the same with everything. Whatever you have, invest it and more will be given to you. The more you invest your talents, the more you will be entrusted with.

The uninformed believe there is a lack in the universe, that those who have more take away from those who have less. The universe does not work in lack. My observation is that those who take on responsibility are given more. Those who shirk responsibility and bury their talent in the ground have it taken away from them and given to someone who will invest it. I have noticed that the more I draw from source (the universe, God), and invest wisely, the more I am given. If I take only a small amount and do nothing with it, even that small amount is taken from me.

In the Biblical parable of talents (Matthew 25:14-30, Luke 19:12-27), the servant who is given one talent (money) by his master to invest, buries it in the ground because he fears losing it. When he tells this to his master, his talent is taken from him and given to the servant with 10 talents—because he has worked his 10 and made 10 more.

The message is simple. When you wisely invest what you have, including money, expertise, or talents, more will be given to you. When you hoard or bury what you have, even your little amount will be taken away.

I believe that anyone can learn to make the shapes they desire with their energy. They can make big or small shapes, vast or minute, globally sprawling or very local. But most people do not. They are either unaware they posses this ability, or they know but fail to use their knowledge out of fear or laziness.

Knowledge is also a talent. It follows the same law: Use it or lose it.

Most people draw a tiny amount of energy from '**the infinite**,' and mould it into a small reality that they create and re-create every single day. Then they complain that there is not enough.

In the Upanishads it says, '*they took abundance from abundance and abundance still remained*.' There is abundance. It is out there. It is ours. We own it and we can do anything we want with it. But we can't take advantage of money if we are afraid of it, or if we are lazy, or ignorant. Neither does it help to stick childish labels across the front saying 'dirty, greedy, bad,' or drilling it into our offspring that creating the money shape will make them bad and banish them to hell fire. When we are constantly told that God does not like rich people, all this negativity gets stuck on the hard drive like a virus. It is really not a wonder then that we consciously or unconsciously avoid learning about, earning, or mastering money.

Let me tell you what my thoughts are about the energy we call money.

Money is God.

Certainly it is a part of God.

Read your bibles please, and see what the prophets have to say on the subject. It seems they all agree: God is omniscient.

He is Omnipotent and He is Omnipresent. He is on the inside and He is on the outside. He is the before and the after. He is the here and the now. God is the Alpha and He is the Omega.

If God is everything, then God is money. Money is a part of everything. There can be no bad in anything other than the bad we bring.

When you talk to people they say, 'there is no money about,' or 'the rich have all the money,' or 'the recession has swallowed all the money up.' But as I said, money is just a shape we make with energy. There is an infinite amount of energy out there just waiting to be converted—but it won't convert itself.

And it will not be converted easily by the lay. History has shown us that much already. To make money, you have to learn how to do it. You have to learn how to convert energy to £'s. You have to study the principles.

If we want to experience more money, then we have to master the art of taking raw energy and making it into cold, hard cash.

As far as I can see, everything that was ever there is still there. We've just stopped looking for it because we believe there is a lack. We are told daily on the news there is a lack.

In reality, there is not a lack of money, because money is

simply a physical representation of energy. What there is, is a lack of people utilizing the energy ever on hand to make the money shape.

So here is my best advice on things fiscal. It is what I offer to myself on a daily basis. It is what I offer to my children, and what I will offer to their children and to anyone else that asks me.

- **First and foremost—create the demand.**

   (Further reading **Live Your Dreams** - by Geoff Thompson)

   If you have no financial demand, there is no necessity for creating money. People tend to earn just about what they need to earn. Increase what you need (the demand) ever so gradually, and that will produce the energy you need to expand. If you keep a gold fish is a small bowl, the fish will stay small. If, however, you place it in a bigger bowl, it will expand to its new environment.

   When I lived in a small house, I created enough money just to pay the bills. With my business growing, I naturally needed a bigger place to work. Despite it being a financial stretch, I brought a house three times the size to enable us to grow. Within three years my product list of books and DVD's expanded from 13 items to more than 30. I increased the demand, and everything else, including me, grew accordingly.

- **Change your language—stop calling money bad (the universe may be listening)**

  (Further reading **The Alchemist** – by Paulo Coelho)

  It is not bad. Money is used to print the bibles of the world. It feeds starving children. If you keep calling it bad you will block its flow towards you.

- **Change perspective.**

  (Further reading **I Can Make You Rich** - by Paul McKenna)

  Possessing money is not greedy. Only hoarding money is greedy, and perhaps even caustic. It is an honour to be a distributor of fiscal wealth. You are a caretaker, and that demands massive responsibility.

- **Study money.**

  (Further reading **The Richest Man in Babylon** - by George Samuel Clason).

  If you want to be a great martial artist, what do you do? You devour everything you can on the subject of martial arts. You study with the masters and you train three times a day. This principle holds true with everything. If you want to be great at something, study it intensely or expect to remain ignorant and poor. Everyone knows this, right? It is common sense. But with the money issue, sense is not so common. It seems to go out the window, and people fall back on good, old luck. They spend a quid a week on a lottery ticket and pray for the fates to favour them.

- **Be brave.**

(Further reading **The Beginners Guide to Darkness** – by Geoff Thompson)

All the information in the world will not help you if you do not use it. Learn the information. Use the information. It takes courage. Courage comes from doing the things you fear—so do the things you fear. This is the essence of being a warrior.

- **Keep the flow.**

(Further reading **The Toa Te Ching -** by Lau Tzu)

If you have money and become afraid of distributing it, money will become a caustic that will damage you and everyone around you. Keep it moving. Bring it in. Move it on. When you stop the flow, you start the atrophy.

- **Be generous.**

  (Further reading **The Secret** - by Rhonda Byrne)

  When you are tight with money and you don't want to share, you announce to the universe that you believe there is a lack. When you do that you create a lack. That is why generous people are so attractive. At some level we know that they know there is abundance, which is why they are happy to share.

- *Do not* **be realistic.** *Do not* **manage your expectations.**

  (Further reading **Losing My Virginity** – by Richard Branson)

  Being realistic is just a small man's way of saying 'think small.' Managing your expectations is just a crap PR term for doing the same thing. If you think realistically, you will always fall short. If I was 'realistic' I'd still be working in the factory, punching way below my weight. Guard against anyone who tells you to be realistic. Sack anyone who wants you to manage your expectations.

- **Do not differentiate.**

  (Further reading **Think and Grow Rich** - by Napoleon Hill)

  Money is not money. It is just a shape we make with

our energy. We can make lots of shapes with our energy and money is just one of them. Don't allow it to become any more or any less than that. If you do, you'll start seeing some things as more important than others. You'll make the mistake of thinking that *some people* as more important than other people.

In spiritual terms, everything is equally important, and everything is equally unimportant. Everything is everything, and everything is God. So ultimately, in the higher echelons of spirituality, a man sweeping the floors in McDonald's is no less important than a man who runs a country. If you start to believe differently you will start to act accordingly—and then you are lost.

7) Intellectual.

I invest a large amount of my income on books and courses to educate myself. I always have at least two or three books on the go at any one time. I come from a very physical, working class world where study and intellectual development were not of paramount importance. We believed that, as working class people, our options were limited. We thought there was no real point in trying to become learned. Those rare few that aspired to break the bounds of their class were seen as pretentious swats. They were snobs, and no one really liked them.

If you had your head in a book at dinner time it was enough to get you a beating from the school knuckle-draggers who did not know any better. Becoming an intellectual was not encouraged, and many of us were perversely proud to be thick. There was rarely a case where the line was crossed and you had a tough kid who was also intellectual. But I know for a fact, that if we'd had even one hard case who aspired to academia, we would have all followed suite. All we needed was one good example to *allow* us.

Years later, I challenged the twisted working class ideals that I had been bottle fed since I was a babe in arms, and became an autodidact. I developed a thirst for knowledge, devouring anything and everything, and developing my own library. I realized that the library was one way of escaping my lot. I wanted to trip the light fantastic, but I was too scared to take a trip even outside the eight gates of my home city. I was scared because I was not informed. I learned to use information to dispel my fears.

Later still, I linked the gathering of information with the acquisition of money. I could sell the new information I had found to other people in search of knowledge. Information, I realized, was capital. I tied the information up with massive experience—the two go hand in hand very nicely. Gathering the information was a vital step in me getting out of the factory, out of the self-regulated class system I was in, and out into the world.

I cannot underestimate the power of the intellect. Also I cannot overstate the joy that comes from learning. I talk to people all the time who proudly tell me they have not read a book for 20 years. They are missing out on so much. Part of the homework in my masterclass is book study. To force students into the habit of reading, I require them to read a list of books that I recommend. Information is expansive. It opens up new possibilities for people. It shows them new realities.

Most people spend their whole life quietly dying because they are afraid to expand their world or create a new one. When the Mexican Shaman Don Juan Matus was schooling Carlos Castaneda in the mystic arts, he told him that his reality was just one room in a house of 100 rooms. With training, he could help him to access the other 99. In fact, he could help him get out of the house.

Books do this. They help you see that your reality is not the only reality. There are hundreds more, thousands more—

actually there are billions more. Information can help you access them all. It is astounding the amount you can learn if you only apply yourself to find the powerful information that is available. Start building your library. Take time out every day to read and study. Even an hour a day will become a 365-hour study course in as little as a year.

8) Spirituality

The final aspect of balance is to develop yourself spiritually. This is one area some people embrace and others eschew. Spirituality appears impotent to many people, especially those of a physical bent. They are physically confident but do not have the power to open up to other realms. This is another example of the truth hidden in plain sight.

The next chapter is dedicated to the spiritual warriors, so I will leave the detail until then.

» Warrior Practice:

For the warrior practice in this chapter I would like to encourage you, firstly to identify your strong and weak areas, and find a balance between the two. Someone who is intelligent, but not physically strong/in shape, should begin a concentrated exercise regime. Start with a couple of sessions a week, and lead up to a consistent daily workout. There is room in everyone's schedule for an hour of hard physical training a day. If you don't think you have the time, think again. It is your time. Arrange it. Arrange it better. Rearrange it. Start working out every day. Make your physical workout the power base of your day. A strong physical infrastructure will enable you to facilitate everything else.

Look at the intellectual powerhouse Condoleezza Rice. She knew that to cope with the pressure of U.S. politics at the very highest level, she needed to be in shape. Because she was so busy, she had to create time to train. She got up every morning at 4 a.m., and did a grueling physical workout. You can be sure that when she walked into a meeting, she had the edge on the other people in the room. Not only was she in fabulous shape, but the discipline of getting up at four every morning built a very sinewy mentality.

If you are a physical person with an under-developed intellect, I would like to encourage you to start a reading regime. First, read a book a month, then a book a week. Start with easy-to-read books, and increase the intensity of the material over a period of time. I would also encourage you to study all the important areas that lead to a successful life, starting with body/mind consciousness and leading out into areas like economics and culture.

Chapter Summary:

The gist of this chapter is to develop yourself in all areas so you are not just a physical warrior who understands combat, an intellectual warrior who understands the cerebral battlefield, or a spiritual warrior who excels in all things esoteric. Rather, I would like to excite you into becoming a multi-faceted warrior so you can (as Kipling says) dine with kings and queens, but never lose the common touch.

Chapter Ten

†

A WARRIOR IS...
SPIRITUAL

It is hard to become a warrior without bumping into God. It's a fact. This is the most important and the most exciting thing that my 50 years on this planet has taught me.

In search of perfection and the warrior way you will be challenged. First physically, then psychologically. When your moral fibre is stretched to its very limits you will fall into the Great Divine, and there you will discover God. But it will not be a God of wrath from biblical lore. He will not be carrying the dogma of religion. What you find will be so absolute, it will be impossible to articulate. If you do not find it, it's not because it is not there. Rather, it is because you are not brave enough or you are not open enough to see.

I am not talking about the archetypal God, of course—the man in the sky with kind eyes and beard. I am talking about the Absolute. God is omniscient, He is Omnipotent and he is Omnipresent. *Split a log you will find me, lift a stone and I'll be there.* People get confused with religion and God. They get confused with spirituality and God. They get their backs up when small-minded people tell them that if they don't follow their particular brand of god, Satan's hellfire will follow.

People are not buying this kind of emotional bullying any more. They want more.

I have a Christian friend who does not believe in the Muslim religion. He thinks that the Holy Quran is a load of rubbish. He quotes the Christian Bible where Jesus says that man can only find God through him. But my friend is thinking very small. He is forgetting that there are two billion Muslims in the world that would disagree with him. I also have a Muslim friend that believes similarly. If you are not Muslim, you are an infidel with a one-way, first-class ticket to a destination called hellfire. He too, is thinking way too small.

There are several billion people in the world that would disagree with *him.* I know Sikhs that believe only in the Guru Granthe Sahib, Jews that are prepared to die for the Kabala, fundamentalists who are literally killing and dying for their god. There are Buddhists who secretly believe that only Gautama got it right, Christians that preach hate for all other religions from their church pulpits, and atheists who hate everyone.

Listen, they can't all be right. They can't all be wrong.

Tolstoy said there was one point on which all religions agreed, which is a good starting point. Love.

I concur. Yet I hear a lot of people saying it, and very few people practicing it. Love is a high frequency. The highest. And as a warrior our aim is to go to the dangerous places. Forget the obvious stop-off points of wealth, weapons, and material power. These things come and these things go, but they do not endure.

If you want to be different, if you are tired of following the crowd, then spirituality is the place to be. I'm not talking about the sickly sweet stuff that lacks power. I am talking about the kind of spirituality that moves mountains, parts seas, and brings people to their knees in awe. You can call it God if you want, but you don't have to. You can call it the universe, the collective unconscious, your higher power, it doesn't really matter. Just know that if you want to be a warrior, then at some point you will bump into it.

When I am on my best game, when I am centred and congruent, I feel as though I am, if not god, certainly a conduit for some great force. And when I access this power, more and more frequently these days, I am patently aware of how little man knows of his true potential.

We are a developing species, of that there can be no doubt. But we are still very lowly evolved—somewhere on the lower rungs of an evolutionary ladder, and struggling. If we are ever in any doubt about this we only need to look at the state of the world: *we still kill people.* We still use violence as a problem-solving tool. We murder murderers on death row and call ourselves intelligent. We go to war with other killers in exotic countries and we call ourselves peacekeepers.

Even if we don't do the killings ourselves, we sanction it with our vote, or we let it happen by not using our vote. If we do not kill people ourselves we certainly elect ministers into government who do it for us, or we fail to vote them out again. Even our anti-war marches are a contradiction in terms. They are largely populated by well-meaning, but angry, vitriolic, and violent men and women.

And whilst we wave an angry banner at our warring politicians to condemn their warmongering, privately many of us understand and empathise with vigilantes who wage private war on pornographers, paedophiles, child killers, and any other unsavoury types that are easy to de-humanise.

Just recently (2010), a British child killer serving life in prison was slashed across the throat by another prisoner in an attack that nearly killed him. There was almost a national outcry of people lauding the attacker. I heard one lady in a shop telling her boyfriend she wished he'd been killed and his attacker set free for attacking him. She even suggested setting the child killer free deliberately, and then telling everyone so the masses could all have their share of the killing.

This is the level at which most people work.

Whilst their attitude is easy to sympathise with, it is neither spiritual nor is it powerful. Of course it is hard to like or understand anyone that hurts a child, but violence, no matter how well intentioned, is still violence. It all falls into the same low frequency. There is no logic in it at all, just blind rage. Take for instance the women who attacks a soldier with the heel-end of her very sharp stiletto and shouts at him *violence is not the answer!*

People try to solve the problems of war with anger, but anger is in the same frequency as war. It feeds war. People attack politicians with eggs to demonstrate that taking our country to war is wrong. But throwing eggs is an act of violence in itself, a war in microcosm. Throwing anything, even in demonstration, just adds to war. There is no intelligence in it whatsoever. This kind of thinking is tabloid, and it only adds to the problem. Our thinking is violent, our talking is violent, and our actions are violent. You see it every day. People kill other people in the name of God, and then call themselves spiritual or religious. They are not spiritual. They are not religious. They are just violent murderers.

There are several frequencies we can access as a species, the highest and most powerful of which is love. The lowest and weakest frequency is violence. Unfortunately, this is the one we go to first and most—probably because it is the easiest to access. The higher frequencies, if accessed and held, will always dissolve the lower frequencies.

Logically then, if you want to dissolve violence, all you need to do is go to a higher frequency. This is powerful spirituality. This is the warrior's fare. It is a metaphysical force that is 80,000 times more powerful that all the others. But here is the rub: the higher frequencies are the hardest to access at will. It takes a lot of training to find the frequency of love and stay there, especially if you are surrounded by people in a lower wave length. Because of this, people tend to stay in the lower echelons.

You cannot be in two frequencies at the same time. You are either in one or you are in the other. In addition, you can't dissolve a violent frequency whilst you are in a violent frequency yourself, no more than you can get rid of black by adding more black.

The Vietnamese Buddhist monk and peacemaker Thich Nhat Hanh preaches this lesson in all his teachings. Many peace protesters arrange angry and violent marches against the wars of the world, thinking they are spiritual warriors. Whilst they are very well meaning, they are still way off the mark. They are just violent people adding to the levy of violence that already exists in the world. Thich teaches passive resistance toward violence. He teaches love as the antidote to war, and he promotes silence as a way of garnering power. He advises his followers that anger exasperates the very problem that it is trying to solve. Like petrol on flames, anger ignites war.

As a fledgling species, we are not very good at this yet. Nevertheless, this should be our ultimate aim. I spent an angry decade using violence to try and stop violence, and all I did was make it worse. Every time I (metaphorically) cut the head off one assailant, another three heads appeared in its place. The more violence I employed, the more violence I created. I could see there was no end to it.

These days I leave my hands in my pockets and I practice

the art of frequency. I access higher realities and I practice killing all my enemies by making them friends. I have successfully dissolved many fractious situations in my own life with love, or more specifically the frequency of love. It is amazingly effective. When we can do this en masse, as a species, there will be no more war in the world. This has not happened as yet, but I live in hope. In the meantime, I console myself with the fact that at least there is no war in my world, which is a great start.

Despite being capable of the most heinous acts of violence, yet we have the capacity to be the most amazing, gentle, and loving species. When we access the divine orbits of benevolence, we have the potential to completely dissolve violence and negativity. But if we access those divine orbits at all, we do it all too infrequently.

» Warrior Practices:

In the warrior practice in this chapter, I would like to encourage you to develop, through reading or conversing, a better understanding of faiths other than your own. If you do not have a specific faith, then a better understanding of all faiths is encouraged. Rather than take the often-bigoted and subjective views of other people or the popular press,

I would encourage you to source your own information and form your own views. Talk with different people from different faiths and see what their thoughts and feelings are. You will be surprised how open people are when you show a genuine interest in their faith.

Some of the books that will inform you are:

The Holy Quran

The Holy Bible

The New Testament

The Old Testament

The Guru Granthe Sahib (Sikh)

The Bhagavad-Gita (Hindu)

The Upanishads

The Sutras

The Toa Te Ching by Lau Tzu (Taoism)

The Divine Comedy by Dante Alighieri

As a practical exercise in connecting to your higher self, meditation is probably the best and most direct method. This was detailed in a previous chapter.

Chapter Summary:

This chapter is about searching for higher truths, accessing celestial frequencies and developing yourself into an Absolute warrior. Not the incongruent kind of warrior, who quotes muscular verse, but still lives a fretful and heathen life. But rather the spiritual warrior, who has mastered himself through 'constant labour and deliberate suffering', and has discovered the metaphysical force that is our real future.

Chapter Eleven

†

A WARRIOR IS...FREE.

A warrior seeks freedom—but first he must discover what freedom actually means. Even if he never quite manages to find it in his short life span, he still must diligently try.

Gurdjieffe laughed at the concept of man thinking he was free. How can he be free when his emotions are still so sensitive to the whims of societal expectation and opinion? You wake up feeling good about your day, only to have your emotions scattered like dropped marbles by the long-faced newsreader, who tells you through the television screen that the economy has taken another dive, or that house prices are at an all time low. Journalists have been sent out deliberately to find a list of such depressing items, because bad news makes good copy.

Currently we live in a lowest-common-denominator society that bombards us with negativity 24 hours a day. It is not information we deliberately chose to access. Rather it is information that is pumped into our front rooms, mostly free of charge, via the popular media. This is not conspiratorial. I don't believe there are people sitting in a room somewhere deliberately trying to make life difficult for you and me. Rather, it is lazy, uninspiring and hapless journalism. The information we receive is of the fast-food, instant gratification variety. It is what we have learned to expect.

What we read in the newspapers and what we watch on the TV is, at best, subjective. Mihaly Csikszentmihalyi, an eminent American psychologist, says the brain is bombarded at any one time by about four million bits of information, of which it can only process approximately 200. These 200 bits of information constitute your living reality. So if your 200 bits are taken from the hourly news bulletins, reading the newspapers and/or talking to your chicken-licking mates who prophesied that they sky is going to fall in at any minute, then your reality is going to be one of a recessionary nature. The information we take in daily can be either a prison or a utopia, depending on the nature of that information and our perception of it.

Most people take what information they are given and never question its authenticity, its source, or its objectivity. A warrior, on the other hand, questions everything. He never takes 'yes' for an answer, and he chooses to source his own information. In so doing, he creates his own reality.

Being free starts with freeing your body and mind. At the moment, they are probably being held hostage by bad information. It sounds like an exaggeration doesn't it? Held hostage! But it is true. That is why people pay a lot of money for good information—it can set them free. Bad information, a lack of information, or even good information not acted upon, creates fear. Fear is the prison that we keep ourselves in.

The warrior starts by recognising that he is being held hostage, that he is locked into a reality that he would like to escape. By accepting this as fact, he starts the process of emancipation. Then he sets about changing the information that he ingests.

If you are currently on a warrior path, you are probably already avoiding the news, eschewing the tabloids, and choosing better company—perhaps not quite knowing why you are doing it. Maybe you are even feeling badly about the fact that you no longer enjoy the things you once did, the company you kept, or the habits that you have formed.

There is no need to feel guilty about this. You are growing

into new orbits. Higher frequencies beckon, which means leaving old living behind. This may cause some friction with people who currently share your orbit. People don't like change, especially when that change involves someone they know or love.

When I first started ascending, I experienced a lot of resistance from the people around me, which caused me to hold back. I was afraid of losing their good opinion of me. In some cases I was frightened of losing them all together. With a few people I felt guilty, as though I was leaving them behind. What I later realised is that you do not leave people behind—some of them just don't come with you. That is *their* choice, not yours. Part of becoming free is following your own path, a path that you create. The reason it is called *the road less travelled by* is because in actual fact, *it is the road never travelled by*. It is bespoke, you cut the path yourself as you walk it. It is hard. But then we are warriors, and we are not in the game of easy.

If you are worried about loved ones not coming with you on your warrior path, don't announce your intentions. Make the changes in your life so gradually that they hardly notice. What people react most badly to is announcement. If you tell them you are going to follow a radical new way, they might well panic and cause more fuss than is necessary.

If, however, you make your journey a little more secret, and make the changes ever so gradually, they may not notice at all. Some things of course might have to be announced. If you want to change jobs, or cities, or partners, it might be wise to let your loved ones in on it. If they shoot the plans down and you find yourself retreating into a scared corner, good. This tells you that you are not ready yet.

How will you know that you are ready? You will be so certain, there will be no room for hesitation—no matter what anyone says. And you will be prepared to fight for your new ideal. If your wife or your husband objects, you will convince them. You will be prepared to do anything to make it a reality.

If I am not certain about a change I am about to make, my plans are very easily shot down. But when I am certain, as I must be if it is going to be a success, I become impervious. It becomes a reality the moment I fully commit. Certainty has such power. It is a skill that we all must practice more.

Being free is really an inside job. It is only our fears that keep us jailed. In the warrior practice for this month, the task will be to root out old fears, old scripts, and false beliefs. Once we sort out the inside, the outside will look after itself.

Here are a few of the obvious areas in life where people lack freedom.

» City.

Many people complain that they are not happy in the city where they live. They talk about how they would love to live elsewhere: London, Edinburgh, Paris, or somewhere by the sea. They talk about it, but they rarely do anything other than talk. If you don't like your city, change it. If changing it is hard, all the more reason to do it. Try a different city. Experience a different culture. Live all around the world if that suits you. But don't pretend that you don't have a choice. You have a choice. You are allowing fear to block your path. Sometimes the country, the city, the street, or even the house you live in, may genuinely be a problem.

I had a friend who lived next door to a violent drunk for three years. It shredded his nerves. When he asked me for advice I simply said, *move to a new house*. He'd never seen this as an option because he felt it would be running away. It is not running away, it is just placing yourself in better soil. Other times people *are* running away, and they think that a change of city is all they need. When they move to a new city, even a new country, they realise that they are still the same person with the same internal problems, just in a different location.

It takes wisdom to know when you should stay and when you should go. Just remember, you always have a choice. Thousands have taken that choice before you, and in the future thousands more will up-sticks and move because they are not happy with where they live. If they can do it, you can do it.

» Job.

Very few people get this one right. Nearly everyone I know has a job they hate. Again, they think they have no choice. You always have a choice. Many of them change jobs, but jump from one menial pot into another. They do not possess the skills, the know-how, or the courage to do anything else. When I was a young man, I hated the menial work I did, but it was all I was qualified to do. I realised that if I didn't grow some new skills, I'd be working in shitholes for the rest of my life. So I studied and I trained myself out of menial employment. Eventually I was able to work for myself. Now I am in the privileged position of only doing the work I love. This did not happen on its own and it did not happen overnight. I had to make myself do it. I had to be patient. It took time.

That time is going to pass whether you invest in it or not, so why not start investing? In five year's time you could be in an entirely new orbit, or still stuck where you are, moaning. It's your choice.

» Marriage.

How many times have you heard people say, *we only stay together for the kids*—as though by staying in a dying or deceased relationship they are making the ultimate sacrifice for their children?

In reality people do not stay together for their children. They stay together because they fear separation. Staying with someone you do not love is living a lie. There is no worse way to bring up children than in a loveless marriage. If there really is no hope for the relationship after you have tried to work it out, it is better to be brave and separate. The kids get to see both of you at your best. They get to see both of you happy.

» Body.

People are trapped inside the wrong body. You see it all the time, usually in the form of a body that is overweight, out of shape, or ill. But it is not the body that traps people. It is their belief that they cannot change it.

Believing that you do not have the ability to change how you look and feel is often just not true. If you are overweight, you have the power to do something about that. What a great challenge.

People do not lack information to make the necessary lifestyle changes. There is plenty of that available. It is usually *purpose* in which they are lacking. The search then should be to find a purpose that is more compelling than the excesses you are indulging in.

If you are out of shape, the same thing applies. Find the purpose to get fit, and fitness will come very quickly.

If you are ill, no matter how ill, the best remedy is to inform yourself, become an expert on your particular malady, and then do everything you can to bring your body back to balance. People have done it before. It can be done.

I have a friend, Jahanzeb, who had bladder cancer. He is a young man with a young family so, as you can imagine, the diagnosis was devastating. Wanting to live, my friend gave himself great hope by deciding to do everything within his power to heal himself. He read everything on the subject of his illness, he mastered his palate so as not to feed his cancer, and he trained hard to get himself fit. He did everything he could to make his body an inhospitable host for this disease. And he was cured.

When you live your life as a warrior, there is

always hope. There is always help out there for you when you help yourself.

» Your mind.

Our thoughts keep us captive. Our thoughts set us free. I have spoken about this throughout the book, and there are a plethora of exercises in previous chapters about training the mind.

» Warrior Practices:

The warrior practice in this chapter falls into two categories: internal and external influences.

» Internal influences.

Our information creates our reality, so the warrior practice for this chapter is to become Guinea Pig A in your own life. With pen and paper, examine all the information you are currently receiving. Look at where it is coming from, and take an honest profit-and-loss inventory on whether or not that information is enhancing your life.

Practice changing the information you are receiving. Instead of watching the news and reading the tabloids, put on documentaries about powerful men and women who changed the world. Instead of believing that recession means lack, look back at the historical recessions. See and learn how the industrious made their fortunes, not just despite hard times, but often because of them.

» Internal influences.

I talked in an earlier chapter about shadows, those small bundles of death that we all carry with us. Invisible to the eye, they are highly insidious and very destructive if left to their own devices. Like a virus, they are working away in the background all the time, dictating the way you live your life. They consist of outdated cultural beliefs, implanted fears, old psychological scars, and limiting beliefs about our self and about the world around us.

The reason most people are unable to really live is because of these shadows. This is really a whole subject in itself, so I will refer you to my other book *Hunting the Shadow*. In brief, you need to remove these viruses if you are ever going to access your full power. In spirituality, this process is called *cleansing*. Dedicated people spend their entire lives clearing outdated beliefs and healing old wounds. It can be a lengthy process, but I have to tell you that it is very worthwhile. Your true treasures are trapped behind these shades. As you start to release them, all sorts of amazing thing will be revealed to you.

There are many therapies that can help you to cleanse. Over the years I have tried them all, with varying degrees of success.

Let your instinct direct you to the one that might be most beneficial, but here are a few to consider:

NLP (Nero Linguistic Programming)

EFT (Emotional Thought Therapy)

Psychoanalysis

Hypnotherapy

Regression Therapy

Tapping

Counselling

Art Therapy

Sharing

If you want to work on your own, you can cry them out, scream them out, or hammer them out. You can also will them out, imagine them out, or run them out—running is always great therapy no matter what you're attempting to fix. You can starve them out by killing the junk food, or climb them out—any extreme sport tends to make the body inhospitable for shadows. Likewise, you can train them out, or you can do it the way famous Glasgow gangster Jimmy Boyle did—sculpt them out. Lastly, you can use my favourite method, write them out.

Another tactic is to buy an old tape recorder and talk them out until they are all spent. Talk until you are empty. This is especially useful if you have *shame blocks*, things that you want to express, but feel too guilty or ashamed to talk about. A tape recorder is an inanimate object that cannot point and whisper. It will not be tracing back the smoke to look for fire. It will not judge you.

Tell it all. Tell each and every detail, especially the seedy ones. Spill all the thoughts that hurt you most. Get out *every* detail. Nothing spared. To the very death.

There is no rush. This can be a slow process. Take your time.

Chapter Summary:

This chapter, this book in fact, is about becoming free! It is about recognising the information prison, inside and outside, and developing techniques to set yourself free. It's about becoming an individual, a warrior, someone who carefully chooses the information he takes in, and the influences he exposes himself to, and creates a bespoke reality. To him, all things are possible.

Chapter Twelve

†

A Warrior...
Mentors Others

One of the things I have learned, and one of the things I know from my own warrior path, is if you want to grow, you need to pass on what you have learned to others.

The more you pass onto others, and the more generous you are with your learning, the quicker you will ascend to the next level. You have to mentor the up-and-coming, the aspirant, so that his path can be fed and nurtured by your lessons. It is only in helping others that we are able to help ourselves.

It is difficult to access new levels of information and knowledge if we do not make room for it by passing on our learned information to other people.

A warrior knows this. That is why he always takes time to

mentor through the spoken word, through the written word, through direct instruction, and through great example.

Most of my own mentoring comes by way of the written word. I write books, articles, newsletters, blogs, stage plays, television and cinema. As a warrior, you should strive to find your own purpose, your personal rich vein of cleansing. Mine is writing, but I also teach martial arts groups, university students, filmmakers, teachers, school kids—anyone that God places in front of me.

As I have grown with age, currently being at the half-century mark and feeling wonderful, I tend to use fewer and fewer words. Too much badinage can flood the message, so I train every day to live my gospel.

This is the most powerful message you can give. When you live it, people know. The congruence is so powerful, and the signature so unique, that people from across the globe will recognise it. The whisper is louder than the shout, as they say. Silence has a power that permeates all things. That's why I spend time every day practicing with nothing. This is hard for me. I am a man who likes to talk. But where I can, I practice saying everything by saying nothing at all.

Francis of Assisi said that every man should preach the gospel, and only if he really had to, should he use words.

Needless to say, as we develop toward this, some words *will* be necessary, especially in the written form. I am sure you would be unhappy if you paid good money for this book, and opened it up to find nothing but blank pages. Silence does not carry so well in books, I have found—though if it did, I could produce a lot more tomes than I am currently outputting. Come to think of it, I could call it the 'book of silence,' and encourage people to open the pages just to stare at the blank sheets. I doubt it would make the *Sunday Times* best-seller list, however.

Writing and teaching are the natural places that I shine. This is my calling. Every bone in my body tells me this is true, so I am following my instinct and practicing every day to finesse my art. As I get better at it, I am able to get my message across with fewer words.

I have yet to meet anyone great at what they do who does not mentor. It seems to go with the territory. I watched the great television writer Paul Abbot doing a lecture once in London, and he told the audience how important it is to mentor and pass on your skills to the next generation. A young lady in the audience asked him, *How do you get to be mentored by Paul Abbot?*

Paul is one of the best writers in the world, so his time

is pretty much filled wall-to-wall with writing commissions. Because of his legend, everyone wants him as a mentor. Paul was very honest. He told the lady that he did not know how you got to be mentored by him. He said that people just gravitated into his orbit at the right time, and it happened organically. One women, he explained, found out where he lived and posted her manuscript through his front door. Another he met almost by accident through a mutual friend. Sometimes people wrote to him, and if he felt the connection, he took them under his wing. He also told how, as a fledgling writer, he had sent his work to famous authors and asked for advice.

I too have had much help from people along the way. I took the first book I wrote (*Watch My Back*) to my local newspaper and asked one of the journalists there, a lady called Sue Lawry, if she would have a look at my work. She was wonderful. Even before she read my words, she complemented me on completing a book. She told me they had 14 full-time journalists in their office, all of whom wanted to write a book. Yet none of them had. She said that just finishing the manuscript was worth celebrating.

After reading the book, she gave me very favourable feedback, explaining where I could expand, and where I could cut. She suggested the points where I was very strong, and she showed me where I needed to work harder. She was my first mentor. I only ever met her once, but she was pivotal in my career as a writer.

Some mentors are like this. They are very important, but they don't mentor you along the whole journey. Other people, like my long-time friend (and fellow playwright) Jim Cartwright, stay in your life a lot longer. Jim was responsible for introducing me to film and theatre. He read my first book and loved it. He contacted me and encouraged me to translate it into film, which I eventually did. Through his influence and friendship I was also inspired to write for the theatre.

Other mentors don't really offer any advice at all. They just doff their hat at you from afar as an indication that you are on the right track. The film director, Ken Loach, very kindly did this for me. When my agent sent him some of my work, he invited me to tea. He told me almost immediately he was not looking for another writer to work with, he just wanted to let me know that he liked the work I was doing.

This is very important when you are developing in any area. When you are unsure about yourself, it is very uplifting to get a nod from one of your heroes. Paul Abbot, who came to mentor me on a film I was writing, told me that the writers who did not stay the course or make the grade were usually the 'greedy ones' who did not take time out to mentor others. I have always remembered that advice.

Mentoring others is also a way of mentoring yourself. It keeps you sharp, and helps you understand your own process. It teaches you humility, and can even inspire you when the person you mentor creates a great piece of work. More than anything else, the giving is a cleansing experience. By cleansing yourself, you open yourself up to be refilled.

The knowledge that I now possess is there as a direct result of the old knowledge that I have passed onto others. It is a vital process, not just for the people you mentor, but also for yourself. When I was first invited to Paul Abbot's house in Manchester, England, I was amazed at the number of people coming and going. It was like Euston Station at rush hour. They were all people that Paul and his fantastic wife, Saska, were helping. He even bought the house opposite so he could fill it with writers he was mentoring.

I have yet to meet a kinder, more generous family. Paul is responsible for an uncountable number of successful writers in this country, and here's the thing. The natural by-product of his mentoring is that the more he gives out, the more he gets back. I have never seen a man with so many writing commissions. He is currently in the U.S. working on a slate of Hollywood projects.

My own experience of mentoring, in the martial arts, in writing, and in life, tells me that you do not really choose the people you mentor. They choose you. Actually, to be more accurate, the universe conspires in a delicious act of serendipity to bring the right people together.

But it is not all a *happy accident*. You have to play your part in the equation by allowing it to happen. It is very easy, and often sorely tempting, to block out the serendipity and say 'no.' When you are very busy, the last thing you want to do is mentor other people. *Where am I going to find the time?* When someone writes to you or calls, it's easy to think, *I just can't. I am so busy*—even though your instinct is saying *Do it. This feels right.*

There is always time. The time belongs to you. It is organised by you, and it is you who gets to set the clock in your day. You actually make time. When you place more into your day, time expands to accommodate. So make more time in your schedule to mentor. It will be worth the while and 10 times more will come back from your tithe than you gave. I guarantee it.

Here are a few pointers when it comes to mentoring,

because unfortunately, not everyone wants your advice. If you are very successful, they often just want your coattails or your contacts. In some cases, they want you to do the work for them.

- **Help those who help themselves.**

    If you lift someone else's weight for them, they will never develop their own physique. In weight training you have someone help you when you lift a heavy weight, called 'a spot.' He will stand behind you when you lift the weight, encourage you, and inspire you, but he will not touch the bar unless he absolutely has to. Even then, he will only do the bare minimum, leaving the majority of the lift to you. Be a spot for those you mentor. Don't lift the weight for them.

- **Be honest.**

    If you are not honest with the person you are mentoring, he will never grow. Line your honesty with kindness, encourage them with everything you say, but never lie. It will not help.

- **Never move the same brick twice.**

   When I was a bricklayer, it was a brutally hard employ. You learned from day one never to move the same brick twice. If a bricklayer was building a wall, your job as his labourer was to calculate how many bricks he needed, and supply them. If he needed 200 bricks, you certainly did not load out 300 for him. If you did, you'd end up having to move 100 of them a second time.

   Mentorship it is the same. If you give people advice and they don't take it, do not give them that advice again. It is too exhausting. I once spent two years mentoring a man before realising he was not taking the advice I was offering. Eventually, I let him go.

- **Listen to your gut.**

   You cannot and should not mentor every single person that asks. Some of them are meant for you, others are not. Let your instinct tell you which is which. I can tell within a minute of talking to someone if we are a match or not. Some people are not meant for you, others are not ready for you yet, and more still never will be ready. The best ones ooze gratitude, and they do the work. The rest are best left alone.

- **Limit your mentoring.**

    It is wise to place a limit on the number of people you mentor. Otherwise you will have a full-time job on your hands , and never get any of your own work done. I once spent an entire day meeting people and mentoring. When I returned home, I realised I had neglected my own commitments. You have bills to pay. The mortgage will not pay itself. So be careful about how many people you mentor.

- **Learn to say no.**

    Some people are fantastic. They ask sparingly, and they respect your time. These are the people you want to help more and more. Other people ask for the world, but when you try to give it to them, it is still not enough. You have to learn to say, 'no.' It's hard. But if you don't, you'll end up doing their work for them.

- **Expect nothing in return.**

    We all like to be thanked. We all want praise and acknowledgement for our good deeds—but mentoring is done best when there is no expectation from the mentor. Mentoring should be about helping for the love of helping. If you expect anything in return, you break the bond. It becomes a bargain, and not a gift. Always try to help, and never keep a record of your deed. That way you will not fall into the trap.

- **Don't look for people to mentor.**

    I have found it is not wise to seek people to mentor. It is better to let them come to you. Better still, allow the relationship to happen organically. When you try to force your instruction on people—no matter how much they need it and no matter how much you want to help—it rarely works.

    I had a lady ring me many years ago whose husband was a big fan of my work. He'd been suffering from depression, so she asked if I would help mentor him through it. I suggested that her husband call me himself. This would enable me to make sure he really wanted help. If he did ring, answering the call would be my first act of mentoring, and his first step to recovery. The very act of saying *I want help* is always the first step.

» Warrior Practice:

The warrior practice in this chapter is to start mentoring today. You will not have to look far for someone to help. If you are successful in any field, the chances are you probably have a queue of people asking you for help. Take on the responsibility. Help someone help themselves. If you are nervous about it, start with one person. As you get better and your confidence grows, expand your list. Keep the rule strict though. Only help those that help themselves. Otherwise your energy will be wasted. You will be casting your pearl before swine.

Chapter Summary:

This chapter is about exploring the need for mentoring, the purpose behind teaching and the joy of seeing yourself expand as you help other people to develop. Mentoring is an excellent form of service, and when you have been on the planet for even a short span of time, you quickly realise that service is the most powerful thing you can do as a human being. All the religions recommend it. The Christians say that when you serve a prisoner you serve God (a literal prisoner, or a person that is imprisoned by addiction or ignorance). The Buddhists also believe that service is the noblest thing we can do as a member of this species. The best thing about service is that when you serve others, your serve yourself.

It is the secret to perpetual motion.

Chapter Thirteen

✝

A Warrior...Serves

It has been said: with great power comes great responsibility. This is common knowledge and it is true. What is also true, but not so commonly known, is that responsibility is a necessary component in developing greater power.

Only the warrior fully understands this. When we serve ourselves, we think and we create small. We develop just enough power to sustain our own individual life. When we serve others however, we take the responsibility of that service on our own shoulders, and we grow both in power and in stature. This is why the warrior does not just serve, he serves prolifically; service is his *raison detre*.

A warrior understands the nature of the reciprocal universe. He knows that what he sows he will also reap. And because he innately understands cause and effect, he uses it to great profit both for himself and for those around him.

And the more people he serves, the more he will be served in return.

He also knows that true and authentic power, the real concentrate, comes from anonymous service and philanthropy. Service that is so secret only you and God know about it is paramount for a warrior. Public service is valid, since it is not always possible to keep charity completely covert. But if you want to secrete pure elixir from your service, then anonymity is the order of the day.

I would not be exaggerating if I said that service is the greatest business secret in the world. Actually, it is a great secret full stop, not just for business, but also for life. Like all spiritual imperatives, this one is hidden in such plain sight that it is invisible to the majority of people who are looking for secrets in the usual places. It is so anti-intuitive that many people are either disappointed when they hear it—because they think that the idea of *service* is corny—or they are immediately dismissive because it does not meet with the dog-eat-dog philosophy of current climates. Some simply think that it is not a tenable option when 'realistic solutions' for 'real problems' are called for.

Those who know me, know that my solutions to opportunities are usually always anti-intuitive. Rarely do they satisfy the *currently-panicking,* I am also not a man who likes to be realistic. If I was being realistic, do you think this factory worker who left school with no qualifications would ever have gone on to trip the light fantastic and live the life of dreams? I think not.

So I ask you to be of expanded consciousness on this subject. I ask you to not think with a majority mentality. All that type of thinking gives you is a mass solution, making you end up as the masses end up, like sheep herding through the wide gate of life. The wide gate is crowded, and according to biblical lore, it leads only to death. Success demands that we muster the courage and enter through the narrow gate. You will find no queues here. That's how you know you are in the right place.

I have been in business of commerce now for 20 years, and I have been in the business of life for 50. This is the greatest secret I have discovered, the most exciting revelation I've had. Service not only offers the ultimate profit, it is also the secret to perpetual motion.

I could tell you that I found this secret in the great books: The Holy Bible, The Testament Old and New, the Bhagavad-Gita, the Guru Granthe Sahib, the Upanishads, the Holy Quaran, the Toa Te Ching, and I would not be lying. I could also tell you that the Nazarene preached this gospel in his sermon on the Mount. He also sent his apostles out into the world to spread the word, as did Mohammad, and Siddhartha, Mother Teresa, and Ghandi. The list is extensive.

As long as man has drawn breath, he has preached the spiritual prophesy and fiscal profit of service. I could tell you all that, and it would be convincing enough for some. It might even confirm what many had always suspected. The fact is, all of these tomes are built on the premise of service. However, if my life experience had not concurred with biblical lore, if living in the world had not taught me the potency of service, then I would have no right to offer it to you as a working tool, or to tell you that in business and in life, service is potentate.

Believe me, my very colourful life living on dangerous edges and searching in hidden corners for the alchemical elixir *has* shown me the absolute and unequivocal power of service. But what is even more delectable is that it is so obvious. It is also very easy to access. It is available to everyone in every situation.

I don't find service to be so valuable simply because it is nice to serve. It does make you feel good, and there is a great satisfaction in serving others in a multitude of ways. It is valuable, it is precious, and it never ever fails to return a profit because the universe is reciprocal. What you put out, will return. If you put out a little, a little will trickle back to you. If you put out a lot, then abundance will be yours to harvest.

What is also great about service—which can be anything from a smile that costs nothing, right through to a £million donation to charity—is that it creates big thinking. As I said at the beginning of the chapter, when you only think of serving yourself, you think locally. You think of your mortgage, your car, your family needs, and perhaps a holiday by the sea twice a year. Because you think about feeding you and yours, you only throw your net out close to the boat, hoping to catch enough fish for your own hungry mouths. This is fine in and of itself. There is nothing wrong with it. But if you want to think huge, then think about ways of feeding hundreds of mouths, or think about ways of serving thousands of people. Actually why not think universally and find ways to serve hundreds of millions?

Ultimately, if you think about serving God (whatever your perception of God is), you will be thinking *god like,* and *big* ideas will start to form in your mind. By doing this, the most amazing opportunities will present themselves to you.

If you have three people in a boat and you want to catch their dinner every day, how inventive would you need to be? Not very. One fishing rod and a bit of bait would do the job. If however, you had to feed 10 people, or 100 people, or if you had 10,000 hungry mouths to find food for, then you would have to become very inventive. You would have to access a bigger boat for a start, and you'd need to embrace bigger and better fishing methods.

If you sit and think about ways to catch three fish a day, you will find ways to catch three fish a day. Your demand and your supply will be matched and equal. You will not develop ways to catch a million fish by thinking about catching three.

Thinking about serving yourself is the same idea. It encourages you to think small. Think about serving others however—the more the better—and you suddenly become a big thinker. You create the demand to become a big thinker. It is scary to think big. It intimidates people. It intimidates me. I can see big ideas in my mind's eye quite easily. The thought of creating them excites me. Yet it scares me too. What if I fail? What if I aim for 100 fish, and don't make the quota? What if I go out into deeper waters and I am out of my depth? What if I sink? What will happen if I catch 100 fish today, and then people expect me to catch 100 fish every day?

How will I cope with the weight of all that responsibility?

You will grow to cope. You will expand. Fear tempers us. Responsibility puts muscle and sinew into our mentality. There is a chance of failure of course. Sometimes we don't make it. Occasionally we do fall. But we keep getting back up again. We do not indulge fear, because as a warrior we know that fear is the mind killer. Fear is at the very core of the warrior's life, always trying to crack him. He does not allow it.

The Oscar-winning film director James Cameron said that failure is always an option, but fear is not.

Because I am in the business of expansive thinking, I put service at the forefront of my day. When I meditate and when I pray, I do not ask God for ideas that will serve me. I ask Him for ideas that will serve Him. In doing so, I am presented with rich-vein-opportunities that serve everyone. Because I am a part of 'everyone' and I am part of God, it also serves me.

Two thousand years before Christ, Hermes concurred. He said that what you gave out would return. So, if you want massive, then give massive. If you want to be a massive conduit for service, then you need to develop the infrastructure to deliver your massive ideas. You will not catch a million fish from a dingy.

Service is not about being a great bloke so you can say to your friends, family and the world at large, 'I do a lot for charity, but I don't like to talk about it.' It is about pragmatic business, fiscal savvy, and helping yourself to abundance by creating abundance for others. If you want to be large, if you want to be magnificent, if you want to thrive, then stop thinking about yourself. Start thinking about others, and you will expand beyond even wild imagination.

You don't have to take my word for any of this. You need to be your own proof.

» Warrior Practices:

The warrior practice for this chapter is to practice the art of service.

Make a list of areas in your life where you can add service, or where you can improve service that is already in place. Start with yourself and work outward to your family, your friends, your work mates/business associates, strangers in the street, and needy people in faraway places. Remember that everything affects everything else. All service is equally worthy. Looking after an elderly neighbour is just as powerful as digging wells in India. But keep in mind that you must be consistent with your service. It is no use raising millions for the needy, while neglecting your own children. Charity starts at home.

Start small. Like a weightlifter who gradually loads heavier and heavier discs onto his bar, we have to expand our service with our ability to serve.

Look for the opportunities that are all around you. Start local. When I first had my epiphany many years ago and discovered the power of service, I said to my wife, *I need to do something big to serve people.* Sharon pointed out the pile of letters and emails from people asking for help. *Why not serve them?* I mistakenly felt that local service of the anonymous kind was somehow not worthy enough. The opposite is true. When you spend half an hour on the phone talking to a stranger and guiding him through his depression, *that is* global. When you save one man, you save the whole word.

» Random acts of service.

Don't let a day go by without at least one act of random service. Anything from returning a call from someone looking for advice, right through to making an anonymous donation to charity.

» Anonymous service.

We have established that there is tremendous power in anonymous service. In fact, this is the most potent of all forms of service. I would like to encourage you to set up a pipe line for anonymous service, something that automatically serves others 24 hours a day, 365 days a year. This could be something small like a direct debit donation to a worthy cause, or something big like buying an old building and anonymously donating it to the homeless. There is massive power here. Huge.

» Secret Santa.

A wonderful man called Larry Stewart, a millionaire businessman from Kansas, USA, knew the power of anonymous service. For the best part of 26 years, he spent each Christmas roaming the streets of Kansas City dressed as Santa, giving out money to the homeless. He didn't just give the odd nickel or dime or dollar, but multiples of $20, $50 and $100 bills. He gave out a total of $1.3 million, all under the guise of Santa Clause. Journalists and civic leaders were mystified for years as to the real identity of the secret Santa. No one knew until after he died, when the truth was revealed to the world.

Is there an area in your life, in your world, or in business where you could be a secret Santa? As one of the warrior's practices in this chapter, I would like to encourage you to try and find one. Set it up. Don't tell anyone.

Chapter Summary:

Service is the warrior's ultimate aim. This chapter is about exploring the varied ways you can expand your consciousness by increasing your service

The number 1 rule is *Serve one, serve all.*

Chapter Fourteen

†

A WARRIOR IS…
KAIZEN

The four enemies of man are fear, false clarity, power and old age. To maintain the discipline that our warrior lives demand, we need to be consistent in our battle against the four enemies. We have to guard all the time against complacency. People often get lost very quickly after finding themselves because of, what they call in the Kabala, *the forgetting*. Purpose and balance are very hard to find and twice as easy to lose. What we pay attention to will grow, and what we take our attention away from will atrophy.

In other words, we lose what we do not use. People have a false assumption that maintaining standard is all about treading water. The opposite is true. If you stand still, you automatically move backwards, because everything else in the universe is constantly evolving.

Kaizen is a Japanese business philosophy for continuous

improvement of working practises and personal efficiency. Everything you have read in this book, all the exercises and practices, need to become a part of your life. It is not a weekend course that you take. It is something you do for life.

I have found that people tend to get inspired by a book or an inspirational conversation and then race at full pelt toward their goal. But sprinters rarely finish first in the game of life, if they finish at all. It is the long distance runner on the steady trot that always takes the goal. This is a lifetime pursuit, not a weekend qualification. If you keep that in mind from the beginning, then a positive end is assured.

I spent the first half of my life looking for the fast track, standing on coattails, sneaking under the wire, and getting into places through the back door. I also practised excess in the hope that 'more' would get me there quicker. Without exception, all of these things failed for me. There is no fast track other than to do the right thing quickly, and stay on the right thing long. Coattails are below the warrior's game. All they do is take you in the wrong direction. Your path is bespoke. You will not find it on someone else's path. Whilst others can guide and inspire you, they cannot take you there. The further you go on someone else's coattails, the further you have to come back again to find your own way.

I have friends who've spent their whole life hitching a ride with other people, not realising that they are getting more and more lost with each passing day. I have one friend, a quite brilliant man in his own right, who has been doing this for the last 30 years. When I saw him recently, I found that he is further behind today than he was when I first met him all those years ago. When you sneak under the wire, you might get the medal or the qualification or the certificate, but you know inside that you haven't earned it. And when you walk into a room, everyone else will know you didn't earn it too—there will be no aura trail following you. Going under the wire and sneaking in through the back door is only good for one thing. It shows you the wrong way to work.

We have all done it, all of us. Part of the journey necessitates taking the wrong turn now and then. But you must always beware. You can take one bad turn too many and never find the way back again. It is OK to do this once, maybe twice, at a stretch. But don't allow yourself to fall for this beginner's trap any more than that. If you want the physique, you need to move some weight.

The things that I have earned in my life are a part of me, and bring with them a certainty that is startling. Everything else is just useless decoration,

Let's remind ourselves of the four enemies:

» Fear.

The first imperative on the ascension into higher frequencies involves mastering the senses. As I said earlier, this all starts with control of the palate. If you are filling your body with fear from the news, tabloids, and environment, you will always keep yourself in a frequency of fear. It's just like staying in a swimming pool will always keep you wet. The physical body must be under your control before you can access and hold powerful frequencies. Whilst you are awash with fear, because of the way you live, this will be an impossibility.

At the higher levels of consciousness, attained through sustained, disciplined living, miracles occur. Your reality becomes as changeable as the clothes on your back, and you will be the one in charge of the wardrobe. This should be incentive enough for you to work hard and work constantly at self mastery. If you take away the things in your life that feed fear, then fear will no longer be a factor in your life. And once you have dealt with fear, everything becomes possible.

» False clarity.

This is what you get when you think you've arrived, but really you are still on the lower rungs of the warrior's ladder.

I have experienced false clarity in many areas of my life in the past, and on more than one occasion. As a bouncer I went through an arrogant phase of thinking that I was a lot more capable than I actually was. This was partly because I had some early success, and partly because other people kept telling me how brilliant I was. The mistake I made was believing them. My overconfidence placed a bloat in my chest and a swagger in my walk. I remember it well. The universe soon gave me a little nudge however, just to remind me of my true level. I got into a fight that nearly saw me mangled. If not for the fact that my three attackers were absolutely useless, I could easily have been killed.

I have never forgotten the lesson. Whenever people told me after that how good I was, I didn't listen to them. I kept myself properly humble, knowing how little I really knew. I allowed myself to be guided by the truth, and only I knew what that was.

Another time, I convinced myself that I had found mastery with my palate. I can remember bragging about how easy it was to control my eating. I was sure that I had arrived. More arrogance. The moment you think you've mastered a thing, especially something as subtle as palate, is the moment you underestimate it.

Addictions and bad habits do lose their power when you evict them, it is true, but they are always looking for a way back in. Arrogance is a back door that addiction always finds. Before you know it, you are addicted again.

The lesson? Never underestimate anything. Always keep your guard up, especially after the battle. It is a vulnerable time. This is why the samurai always tightened their helmet straps after the fight. In all my cases of false clarity, the universe quickly knocked the arrogance out of me. The universe, you will find, does not deal in arrogance.

They say that if you meet the Buddha on the path, kill the Buddha. In other words when you think you have arrived, the very act of thinking it will tell you that you haven't.

» Power.

Everyone it seems, wants power. The very act of wanting it, especially when you want it without any sacrifice and in a hurry, is usually an indication that you are not yet ready for it. As Lord Action said, *power corrupts, and absolute power corrupts absolutely*. He noted also that nearly all great men were bad men. It is not always true, but history tells us that it *nearly* always is. The key is to have power, and use it only to the good. The whole premise of JRR Tolkien's epic book, *Lord of the Rings*, is the struggle for, and the battle with, power.

In the book, power is represented by a ring that corrupts almost everyone that touches it. The weaker players are consumed with the lust for power by the mere presence of the ring. The wisest players know their level, and they respect the ring's power enough never to touch it. Those who already have a high-degree power, used the ring to test their power by resisting its lure. Lady Galadriel, who was seven thousand years old and thought to be one of the most powerful Elves that ever lived, passed this test.

The only one in the story that could successfully hold the ring for any length of time was Frodo. He remained uncorrupted because of his childlike character. He lived a simple and joyful life, not wanting any more than he already had. No amount of power could buy or sell him, so the ring had no hold over him. The ring had nothing that Frodo wanted.

If you want nothing, then no *thing* can corrupt you or threaten you.

This is what real power is. The path of the warrior, the hero's journey, is all about creating that simple and fearless life with the elixir of our hard-won experience. This will always be *our attempt*, as Rainer Maria Rilke so poetically put it, even if we *can never achieve the last.*

Those that have real power hold it with reverence—and usually with reluctance. They have it only because they were brave enough to hear *the call to adventure.* The warrior's pilgrimage is a necessary preparation.

In the Star Wars trilogy, Luke Skywalker has to endure a painful pilgrimage before he is let loose with any amount of power. He goes to the swamp planet of Dagobah to train with a 900-year-old Jedi master called Yoda, who has been training knights for more than eight centuries.

The pinnacle of Luke's training is to fight his ultimate nemesis. He is sent into the jungle to do battle with this monster, not knowing who he is or what he might look like. He is confronted by—and duels with—Lord Darth Vader. Luke eventually manages to subdue his great enemy. But when he removes Vader's helmet, he finds his own face under the mask. Vader is Luke—or certainly what Luke could become if he allowed himself to be corrupted by power.

This is no mere action film. The scriptwriter and director, George Lucas, said that Star Wars was directly influenced and shaped by ancient mythology, specifically a book called *The Hero with a Thousand Faces,* by Joseph Campbell.

Campbell, and by turn Lucas, detailed the hero's journey

thus: The initiating call to adventure, the supernatural aids spirited into help the warrior, crossing the first threshold from the old life to the new world, entering the belly of the whale where the hero completely loses his old self and immerses fully into his new reality, right through to collecting the elixir from the journey, and returning in one piece to share what he has learned with others.

If you want power, you have to earn power. You need to sculpt the physical, psychological, and spiritual infrastructure to be able to handle it.

That is what this book is all about.

When you watch Spiderman or Superman and the hero says the immortal line *with great power comes great responsibility,* he is not kidding.

It demands a Titan's strength and a sage's courage to hold power.

» Old age.

Age is one of the four enemies of man. It's true—and it isn't true. If you see age as an issue, then age will surely be an issue. If you don't see it as an issue, and really believe it, then age will not be an issue. As far as I can see, age is a state of mind. You will have heard this advice a million times and discarded it just as many I am sure. Because it can't be true, can it?

No it can't. And yes it can.

Jonathon Livingston Seagull, a fictional bird from a book of the same name by Richard Bach, is a Seagull that is trying desperately to break the bounds of his small winged body. Unlike the other seagulls that are happy to scavenge for scraps on the beach, he wants to challenge the very reality that he has been born into. He struggles to fly harder and higher and faster. He is trapped, not by the circumspection of his body, but by his very limiting beliefs. He is advised by a benevolent narrative voice in the book, that everything from the tip of his right wing, across to the tip of his left wing and all in between, is nothing but his own thoughts made visible. If he can break the bounds of his thinking, then he can break the bounds of his body.

Most people are brought up to believe that everyone under the age of 30 years is young, those between the age of 30 and 50 are middle age, and everyone over and above is old and waiting to die. If you've had this drilled into you all day and every day by those close to you and by society as a whole, then of course that belief is going to be your entire reality.

Like some huge and hideous social experiment you will very probably, like everyone else, fulfil the prophecy. If however, like Lewis Carol's Alice in her wonderland, you realise that this is your dream and you get to dictate what happens in it, you can change the rules. You can re-write the prophecy, and, if you choose, you can still be adventuring for another 100 years.

There was a 101-year-old man called Buster Martin who completed a marathon, 26.2 miles, in 2008. Another man, Fauja Singh, was 98 years old when he ran the London Marathon in 2010.

Change your thinking and you will remain ageless.

» Warrior practices:

The only practice necessary here is vigilance.

As a warrior, you must constantly assess your development and growth. If things are not growing, or if they are starting to atrophy, then you should retrace your steps. Identify what you have changed or what you are doing wrong, and then get back onto the path.

Chapter Summary:

This chapter is about the necessity of continual self-improvement so that the *found man* does not become the lost soul.

Acknowledgements

Thank you to K T Forster for some of the inspired ideas in this book.